The Elementary Mathematics of the Atom

Man's knowledge of the atom—its nature, its structure, its behavior—is expressed in the language of mathematics. He who wants truly to understand the atom, the unlocking of whose secrets has opened the way for the greatest leaps forward in the history of technology, must approach it through mathematics. It has been generally assumed that the mathematics needed is highly advanced. But in this book Irving Adler shows that considerable knowledge of the atom can be understood by any interested person who has had one year of high school algebra.

Without resort to calculus, it achieves the following:

Develops in some detail the molecular theory of matter and the periodic table of the elements (Chapter II).

Assuming some well known relationships of motion, electricity, and light, derives others by elementary methods (Chapters III, IV, and V).

Using these relationships, develops in detail the Bohr model of the atom with circular electronic orbits (Chapter VI).

After describing the basic concepts of the quantum-mechanical model of the atom, shows how its principal conclusions explain the periodic table of the elements (Chapter VII).

THE ELEMENTARY MATHEMATICS OF THE ATOM
by
Irving Adler

"This book succeeds in illuminating some of the more theoretic aspects of modern physics and chemistry by the use of simple mathematics...it brings down to the level of the bright, interested high school science student, or intelligent layman, areas of science previously available only to the college physics major. Recommended for any library." LIBRARY JOURNAL

This popular level study develops and examines in some detail the molecular theory of matter and the models of atomic structure." NEW TECHNICAL BOOKS (A Selective List, 1965), NEW YORK PUBLIC LIBRARY

THE ELEMENTARY MATHEMATICS OF THE ATOM

Books by Irving Adler

COLOR IN YOUR LIFE
DUST
THE ELEMENTARY MATHEMATICS OF THE ATOM
FIRE IN YOUR LIFE
HOT AND COLD
HOW LIFE BEGAN
INSIDE THE NUCLEUS
MAGIC HOUSE OF NUMBERS
MAN-MADE MOONS
MONKEY BUSINESS: *Hoaxes in the Name of Science*
A NEW LOOK AT ARITHMETIC
THE NEW MATHEMATICS
PROBABILITY AND STATISTICS FOR EVERYMAN
THE SECRET OF LIGHT
SEEING THE EARTH FROM SPACE
THE STARS: *Stepping Stones into Space*
THE SUN AND ITS FAMILY
THINKING MACHINES
TIME IN YOUR LIFE
TOOLS IN YOUR LIFE
THE TOOLS OF SCIENCE
WEATHER IN YOUR LIFE
WHAT WE WANT OF OUR SCHOOLS
THE *REASON WHY* BOOKS (*with Ruth Adler*)

IRVING ADLER

THE ELEMENTARY
MATHEMATICS
OF THE ATOM

With diagrams by Ruth Adler

The John Day Company
New York

Contents

THE ELEMENTARY MATHEMATICS
OF THE ATOM

I

Mathematics and the Atom

Unseen, but Well Known

NOBODY has ever seen an atom. Nevertheless we have a large amount of knowledge about atoms. We know that there are about one hundred different kinds of atoms, and that they are the building blocks out of which all chemical substances are made. We can describe their *outward behavior,* in which they interact with each other to form molecules, or with particles of light that they may send out or receive. We can also describe their *inner structure,* built out of a central core called the nucleus, and planetary electrons that surround the nucleus. We can explain, too, how their outward behavior is determined by their inner structure. All this knowledge is formulated in the language of mathematics.

Mathematics Enters the Picture

In the study of the atom, as in any science, mathematics plays a part in three ways. The first role of mathematics in a science is purely *descriptive.* In the course of his experiments a scientist measures certain quantities and observes relationships among them. He then describes the observed relationships by means of an appropriate mathematical equation or inequality. As examples we cite two equations that we shall have occasion to use in Chapter II.

Temperature measurements in a scientific laboratory are ordinarily expressed in terms of the Celsius scale, on which the freezing point of water is 0° and the boiling point of water is 100°. The study of the behavior of heat engines led to the introduction of another scale known as the Kelvin scale. On the Kelvin scale the freezing point of water is 273°, and 0° is the absolute minimum temperature that may be approached but can never be attained. The relationship between a Celsius temperature T_C and the equivalent Kelvin temperature T_K is given by the equation

$$(1) \qquad T_K = T_C + 273.$$

When a sample of gas is enclosed in a container we can measure its volume, its pressure, and its temperature. If we multiply the number of units in the volume by the number of units in the pressure, and then divide the product by the number of degrees Kelvin in the temperature, a definite number is obtained. Now suppose that the sample of gas is compressed or expanded or heated or cooled, so that its volume, pressure and temperature are altered. If the same computation is made with the new volume, pressure, and Kelvin temperature, the number obtained is found to be about equal to the one obtained before, if the pressure in both cases is low. This observation shows that the volume, pressure, and temperature of a given sample of gas are not entirely independent, but are related to each other. If P is the pres-

10

sure, V is the volume, and T is the Kelvin temperature, the relationship is expressed by the approximate equation

$$(2) \qquad \frac{PV}{T} = K, \quad \text{or} \quad PV = KT$$

where K is a fixed number.

The second role of mathematics in science is *predictive*. By using mathematical techniques to explore the logical implications of known relationships, we can obtain new relationships from old ones, and we can compute quantities instead of measuring them directly. For example, suppose the original values of the pressure, volume and Kelvin temperature of a gas sample are P_1, V_1, and T_1 respectively, and suppose that altered values for the same sample are P_2, V_2, and T_2 respectively. Then, by equation (2), we have $P_1V_1 = KT_1$, and $P_2V_2 = KT_2$. Dividing these two equations, we get the proportion

$$(3) \qquad \frac{P_1V_1}{P_2V_2} = \frac{T_1}{T_2},$$

which relates the new values of P, V and T to the old ones. By using equation (3), if we know the volume of the gas at a given temperature and pressure, we can compute what the volume would be at another temperature and pressure. We shall use it for this purpose on page 36.

Mathematics Makes the Picture

The third role of mathematics in science is *explanatory*. It assumes this role when the scientist constructs a mathematical model of the phenomenon he is studying. The mathematical model is a set of assumptions that he makes for the purpose of explaining the observed rela-

11

tionships. The observed relationships are considered to be explained if they are derivable as logical consequences of the assumptions made in the model. If, in addition, other observable relationships that are implied by the model are verified, then the model is considered to be a substantially true picture of the phenomenon being investigated. An example of such a model is the molecular theory of matter. The basic assumptions of this theory are that every chemical substance is made up of units called molecules; that each molecule is an assemblage of atoms held together by electrical forces; that the nature of a molecule depends on the kind of atoms that compose it, the number of each kind, and the way they are arranged in the molecule; and that all molecules of the same substance have the same composition, while molecules of different substances have different compositions. As it is worked out in detail, the theory specifies the actual composition of each kind of molecule. It tells us, for example, that a water molecule consists of two atoms of hydrogen joined to one atom of oxygen, that an oxygen molecule in the air we breathe consists of two atoms of oxygen, and so on.

Models of the Atom

In order to explain the behavior of atoms, physicists have constructed several different models of atomic structure. The first of these that was fairly successful was the Bohr model of the atom. In this model, Bohr assumed that each planetary electron in an atom revolves about the nucleus in a circular orbit. Sommerfeld constructed a refinement of this model that was in better agreement with the facts by assuming that electron orbits are elliptical. The Bohr-Sommerfeld model has since been replaced by the quantum-mechanical model constructed by Heisenberg, Born, Jordan, DeBroglie, Schrödinger and Dirac, in which the idea that an electron moves in an orbit is discarded altogether.

The Scope of this Book

Both elementary and advanced mathematical techniques were used to construct the molecular theory of matter and the models of atomic structure and to deduce their implications. Fortunately, significant parts of the theories and their consequences can be developed by elementary methods alone. In this book we examine in detail aspects of the theories that require no more knowledge of mathematics than one year of high school algebra. Wherever we have to use a result that can be derived only by using advanced methods, we shall state the result without proof. In spite of this self-imposed limitation on the techniques we use, we shall be able to accomplish the following goals; 1) Relying on some basic laws of chemistry, we shall develop in some detail the molecular theory of matter, and its crowning achievement in chemistry, the periodic table of the elements. (Chapter II) 2) Assuming some well-known relationships of motion, electricity, and light, we shall derive some others by elementary methods. (Chapters III, IV and V) 3) Using these relationships, we shall develop in detail the Bohr model of the atom with circular electronic orbits. (Chapter VI) 4) After describing in simple terms and relating to a simple picture the basic concepts used in the quantum-mechanical model of the atom, we shall show how its principal conclusions serve to explain the periodic table of the elements. (Chapter VII)

II

The Atom in Chemistry

Atomic Theories, Old and New

AS long ago as 420 B.C., the Greek philosopher Democritus of Abdera expounded the view that all matter consists of combinations of small unit particles called *atoms*. At that time this view was only an inspired guess. It was purely speculative, and not related to any particular body of fact. The modern atomic theory of matter, initiated by John Dalton in 1805, has a different character. It is based on a multitude of facts uncovered by the sciences of chemistry and physics, and it successfully explains these facts. In this chapter we outline the chain of thought, based on the facts of chemistry, that led to the formulation and elaboration of Dalton's Atomic Theory.

Mixtures vs Pure Chemicals

All matter is made up of chemicals. Some samples of matter are *pure chemicals,* each of which has uniform properties by which it can be distinguished from every other. Other samples of matter are *mixtures* of these pure chemicals. The distilled water you add to an automobile battery is a pure chemical. So are the oxygen administered from tanks in a hospital, and the carbon deposited as soot on a cold spoon held in a candle flame. Air, on the other hand, is a mixture of the pure chemicals nitrogen and oxygen with small amounts of carbon dioxide and water vapor, and traces of some others. The science of chemistry is chiefly concerned with the properties of pure chemicals that are expressed in the relationships of the chemicals to each other.

Chemical Reactions

The central fact of chemistry is that some chemicals can be changed into others in *chemical reactions*. In one kind of reaction, two or more chemicals *combine* to form another. For example, if hydrogen gas is burned in air, the hydrogen combines with oxygen from the air to form water vapor. In a second kind of reaction, the opposite process takes place, and a single chemical is *decomposed* to produce two or more others. For example, water can be decomposed by intense heat or by an electric current to produce hydrogen and oxygen. Reactions of combination and decomposition show that some chemicals are related to each other as *parts* and *wholes*. Thus, hydrogen and oxygen are the parts out of which water is made. Water is one possible whole that can be obtained by combining hydrogen and oxygen in a certain proportion. Hydrogen peroxide, used as an antiseptic, is another different whole made from the same parts combined in a different proportion. A third type of reaction consists of a reshuffling of parts whereby some combinations are broken up and new combinations are formed from their parts.

16

Compounds vs Elements

While water can be decomposed into hydrogen and oxygen, neither hydrogen nor oxygen can be decomposed into other chemicals. Chemicals that can be decomposed are called *compounds*. Those, like hydrogen and oxygen, that cannot be decomposed, are called *elements*. The elements are the chemical parts out of which all compounds are made. There are hundreds of thousands of different chemical compounds. There are only about one hundred different elements from which all these compounds are made. Each of the elements is usually designated by a special symbol, such as H for hydrogen, O for oxygen, C for carbon, etc. A list of the chemical elements appears in the table on page 48.

Five Fundamental Laws

Near the end of the eighteenth century a decisive change was introduced in the way in which chemical reactions were studied. Whereas chemists in the past had observed *which* chemicals entered into a reaction and which chemicals emerged from it, they began then to measure *how much* of each chemical was involved in the reaction. By weighing the chemicals they determined their masses, because the number of grams in the mass of a body is equal to the number of grams in its weight at sea level. In the case of gases, they also measured their volumes. When it became clear from the experiments of Boyle, Charles, and Gay-Lussac that the volume of a gas depends on its pressure and temperature, careful measurements were made of the pressure and temperature, too. An examination of the quantities of chemicals that entered into and came out of reactions revealed some significant regularities that were summed up in five basic laws of chemistry:

I. *The Law of Conservation of Mass.* (Lavoisier, 1774) *The total mass of the chemicals that enter into a reaction is equal to the total mass of those that are produced by it.* For example when 1 gram of hydrogen combines with 8 grams of oxygen to produce water, the mass of the water produced is 9 grams.

II. *The Law of Constant Proportions.* (Proust, 1797) *The elements that combine to form a given compound are always the same, and the masses of the combining elements always have a fixed ratio that is characteristic of the combination.* For example, the only elements that can combine to form water are hydrogen and oxygen, and the ratio of their masses is always 1:8. That is, in the formation of water, 1 gram of hydrogen combines with 8 grams of oxygen, 2 grams of hydrogen combine with 16 grams of oxygen, etc. In general, if x grams of hydrogen combine with y grams of oxygen to form $x + y$ grams of water, then x and y satisfy the proportion $\dfrac{x}{y} = \dfrac{1}{8}$.

III. *The Law of Multiple Proportions.* (Dalton, 1804) *A given amount of an element may combine with different masses of a second element to form different compounds. But then the masses of the second element that enter into such combinations are always whole number multiples of one particular mass.* For example, 16 grams of oxygen can combine with either 1 gram of hydrogen to

18

form hydrogen peroxide, or 2 grams of hydrogen to form water. Notice that the masses of hydrogen that may combine with 16 grams of oxygen are whole number multiples of 1 gram. (1 gram $= 1 \times 1$ gram; 2 grams $= 2 \times 1$ gram.) Similarly, 3 grams of carbon can combine with either 4 grams of oxygen to form carbon monoxide, a deadly gas in automobile exhaust fumes, or 8 grams of oxygen to form carbon dioxide, the gas that is dissolved in soda water. Notice that the masses of oxygen that may combine with 3 grams of carbon are whole number multiples of 4 grams. (4 grams $= 1 \times 4$ grams; 8 grams $= 2 \times 4$ grams.) A particularly impressive example is given by the combinations that nitrogen may form with oxygen. Seven grams of nitrogen can combine with either 4 grams of oxygen to form nitrous oxide, or 8 grams of oxygen to form nitric oxide, or 12 grams of oxygen to form nitrous anhydride, or 16 grams of oxygen to form nitrogen dioxide, or 20 grams of oxygen to form nitric anhydride. Notice that the masses of oxygen that may combine with 7 grams of nitrogen are whole number multiples of 4 grams. (4 grams $= 1 \times 4$ grams; 8 grams $= 2 \times 4$ grams; 12 grams $= 3 \times 4$ grams; 16 grams $= 4 \times 4$ grams; 20 grams $= 5 \times 4$ grams.)

IV. *The Law of Equivalent Proportions.* (Richter, 1791) *If two elements each react with a third element, and also react with each other, the masses of the two that react with a given mass of the third element will react with each other, or simple multiples or fractions of these masses of the two elements will react with each other.* For example, 1 gram of hydrogen and 35.5 grams of chlorine, each of which are capable of reacting with 8 grams of oxygen to form water and chlorine monoxide respectively, combine with each other to form hydrogen chloride. On the other hand, while 6 grams of carbon react with 8 grams of oxygen to form carbon monoxide, only 3 grams of carbon, or ½ of 6 grams of carbon, react with 35.5 grams of chlorine to form carbon tetrachloride.

In order to standardize the comparison of reacting masses of different elements, it is customary to measure the mass of any element that reacts with exactly 8 mass units of oxygen. The masses determined in this way are called "equivalent weights." An element may have more than one equivalent weight, because, as we have seen, it may combine with oxygen in several different ratios by weight to form different compounds. Thus, the equivalent weight of carbon in carbon monoxide is 6, but the equivalent weight of carbon in carbon dioxide is 3.

V. *Law of Constant Ratios by Volume.* (Gay-Lussac, 1808) *When gases enter into a reaction or are produced by it, the ratio of their volumes, measured under the same conditions of temperature and pressure, can be expressed as a ratio of small whole numbers.* For example, when hydrogen combines with oxygen to form water vapor, the volumes of the hydrogen and oxygen (at fixed temperature and pressure) have the ratio 2:1; the volumes of the oxygen and water vapor have the ratio 1:2. Or, putting it another way, 2 volumes of hydrogen combine with 1 volume of oxygen to form 2 volumes of water vapor. Here are some other combining ratios by volume in reactions for which we have already given the combining ratios by mass:

2 volumes of nitrogen combine with 1 volume of oxygen to form 2 volumes of nitrous oxide; 2 volumes of nitrogen combine with 2 volumes of oxygen to form 4

volumes of nitric oxide; 2 volumes of nitrogen combine with 3 volumes of oxygen to form 2 volumes of nitrous anhydride; 2 volumes of nitrogen combine with 4 volumes of oxygen to form 4 volumes of nitrogen dioxide; 2 volumes of nitrogen combine with 5 volumes of oxygen to form 2 volumes of nitric anhydride.

Dalton's Atomic Theory

In 1805 John Dalton formulated his atomic theory of matter. The theory is a mathematical model designed to explain why chemical reactions obey the five laws described above. Dalton was guided toward the ideas embodied in the theory by a significant clue that is inherent in the Law of Multiple Proportions. As an example of this law, we have cited the fact that while 7 grams of nitrogen can combine with several different amounts of oxygen, these amounts are not arbitrary, but are all multiples of 4 grams. Notice that there is a smallest amount of oxygen with which 7 grams of nitrogen can combine, namely 4 grams, and that increases above this amount can occur only in increments that are equal to it. To understand the significance of this clue, let us examine first a familiar analogy. Suppose you are making a necklace out of ribbon. Since a roll of ribbon is continuous, you may choose any arbitrary length for the necklace, and cut this length of ribbon from the roll to make the necklace. On the other

A length of ribbon is continuous

21

hand, if you are making the necklace of uniform beads placed side by side, you cannot choose any arbitrary length. There is a smallest length your string of beads may have, namely the diameter of one bead, and increases above this length can take place only in increments that

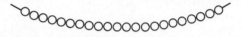

A string of beads consists of discrete units

are equal to it. The amount of oxygen with which 7 grams of nitrogen can combine resembles in this respect the length of a string of beads, rather than the length of a piece of ribbon. This resemblance suggests that, just as a string of beads is not continuous, but is made up of discrete units, a quantity of oxygen is also not continuous, but is made up of discrete units. This is the fundamental idea that Dalton derived from the Law of Multiple Proportions and elaborated in his Atomic Theory. Dalton's theory consists essentially of the following assumptions:

1. Any sample of a compound, or of an element in the free state (that is, not combined with other elements in a compound), is an assemblage of discrete units called *molecules*.

2. There is a smallest unit of any element that may enter into chemical combinations. This smallest unit is called an *atom*. Atoms of the same element are all alike. Atoms of different elements have different masses and differ in their chemical and physical behavior.

3. Every molecule is a combination of a definite number of particular kinds of atoms. Molecules of the same compound have the same composition. The mass of a

22

molecule is the sum of the masses of the atoms that it contains.

4. In chemical reactions, atoms are combined, separated, or reshuffled, but never created or destroyed.

Chemical Formulas and Equations

According to assumption 3, the composition of a molecule is specified by stating which atoms are in it, and how many of each atom it contains. This is done by means of a molecular formula in which each kind of atom in the molecule is represented by the appropriate symbol, and the number of atoms of each kind in the molecule is represented by a subscript of the symbol. For example, as we shall see later, a molecule of hydrogen contains 2 atoms of hydrogen, so the formula for a molecule of hydrogen is H_2. A molecule of oxygen contains 2 atoms of oxygen, so the formula for a molecule of oxygen is O_2. A molecule of water contains 2 atoms of hydrogen and 1 atom of oxygen, so the formula for a molecule of water is H_2O, where the absence of a subscript for the symbol O means that it is understood to be 1.

A chemical reaction is described by means of an equation in which the molecules that enter the reaction are listed on one side, and the molecules produced by the reaction are listed on the other side. Where more than one molecule of a kind occurs, the number of such molecules is indicated by a coefficient written to the left of the molecular formula. Thus, while H_2 means one molecule of hydrogen, $2H_2$ means two molecules of hydrogen. An arrow in the equation shows the direction in which the reaction progresses. According to assumption 4, *the num-*

23

ber of atoms of each kind that occur on one side of an equation must be the same as the number of atoms of each kind that occur on the other side of the equation. However, the grouping of the atoms in molecules changes as a result of the reaction. For example, suppose we want to write the equation for the reaction in which hydrogen combines with oxygen to form water. At least one oxygen molecule must participate in the reaction. However, a single oxygen molecule, O_2, contains two oxygen atoms. To form water with these oxygen atoms, we must provide two hydrogen atoms for each oxygen atom, since the formula for a water molecule is H_2O. That is, we need four hydrogen atoms. This can be provided by two molecules of hydrogen whose molecular formula is H_2. But four atoms of hydrogen and two atoms of oxygen provide enough raw material to make two molecules of water. Consequently the formula for the reaction is

$$2H_2 + O_2 \rightarrow 2H_2O.$$

Notice that the number of hydrogen atoms on each side of the equation is 4, and the number of oxygen atoms on each side is 2.

Explaining the Basic Laws

If Dalton's Atomic Theory is a good model of the constitution of matter, we should be able to derive from it the five basic laws governing chemical reactions. We now proceed to derive them, one at a time.

I. Under the assumptions of Dalton's theory, the atoms that enter into a reaction are the same as the atoms that come out of it. Only their grouping is altered. Conse-

24

quently the total mass of the atoms that enter into the reaction is the same as the total mass of the atoms that come out of it. But the mass of any molecule in the reaction is the sum of the masses of its atoms. Therefore the sum of the masses of the molecules that enter into the reaction is equal to the sum of the masses of the molecules that are produced by the reaction. This establishes the Law of Conservation of Mass as a consequence of Dalton's theory. For example, consider the reaction whose equation is

$$2H_2 + O_2 \rightarrow 2H_2O.$$

Let m_H represent the mass of a hydrogen atom, and let m_O represent the mass of an oxygen atom. Then the mass of a hydrogen molecule is $2m_H$, the mass of an oxygen molecule is $2m_O$, and the mass of a water molecule is $2m_H + m_O$. The total mass of the molecules on the left side of the equation is $2(2m_H) + 2m_O$, or $4m_H + 2m_O$. The total mass of the molecules on the right side of the equation is $2(2m_H + m_O) = 4m_H + 2m_O$.

II. Suppose we use any arbitrary mass of oxygen, and combine it with as much hydrogen as is necessary in order to form water from all the oxygen and hydrogen used. According to Dalton's theory, the oxygen is an assemblage of oxygen molecules. Let the number of molecules in this assemblage be n. Since the equation for the reaction shows that every oxygen molecule combines with two hydrogen molecules to form water, then n oxygen molecules combine with $2n$ hydrogen molecules to form water. The mass of $2n$ hydrogen molecules, each of which has mass $2m_H$, is $2n(2m_H)$, or $4nm_H$. The mass of n oxygen molecules, each of which has mass $2m_O$, is $n(2m_O)$, or

25

$2nm_O$. Then the ratio of the mass of hydrogen to the mass of oxygen with which it combines to form water is

$$\frac{4nm_H}{2nm_O} = \frac{(2m_H)2n}{(m_O)2n} = \frac{2m_H}{m_O} \times \frac{2n}{2n} = \frac{2m_H}{m_O} \times 1 = \frac{2m_H}{m_O}.$$

That is, the ratio has the fixed value $2m_H : m_O$, independent of the number n of oxygen molecules used. This establishes the Law of Constant Proportions for this reaction. A similar argument establishes it for every reaction.

III. Suppose we take an arbitrary mass of nitrogen and combine it with as much oxygen as is needed to form in turn each of the five compounds of nitrogen and oxygen listed on page 19. Whatever each amount of oxygen may be, it consists, according to the Dalton theory, of a whole number of oxygen atoms. Consequently the mass of each amount is a whole number multiple of m_O. This establishes the Law of Multiple Proportions for combinations of nitrogen and oxygen. A similar argument establishes it for all other combinations of two elements. To be more specific in the case of compounds of nitrogen and oxygen, we must use the molecular formulas for them. The molecular formula for nitrogen is N_2. The molecular formulas for the five compounds of nitrogen and oxygen listed on page 19 are N_2O, NO, N_2O_3, NO_2, and N_2O_5 respectively. The minimum numbers of molecules of nitrogen and oxygen that are needed to form each of these compounds are indicated in the following equations:

$$2N_2 + O_2 = 2N_2O,$$
$$N_2 + O_2 = 2NO,$$
$$2N_2 + 3O_2 = 2N_2O_3,$$
$$N_2 + 2O_2 = 2NO_2,$$
$$2N_2 + 5O_2 = 2N_2O_5.$$

26

In order to show the same amount of nitrogen in each equation, multiply the second and fourth equations by 2. Then we have,

$$2N_2 + O_2 = 2N_2O,$$
$$2N_2 + 2O_2 = 4NO,$$
$$2N_2 + 3O_2 = 2N_2O_3,$$
$$2N_2 + 4O_2 = 4NO_2,$$
$$2N_2 + 5O_2 = 2N_2O_5.$$

According to these equations, 2 nitrogen molecules can combine with 1 oxygen molecule, or 2 oxygen molecules, or 3 oxygen molecules, or 4 oxygen molecules, or 5 oxygen molecules. The masses of these five different amounts of oxygen are $2m_o$, $2(2m_o)$, $3(2m_o)$, $4(2m_o)$, and $5(2m_o)$ respectively. Then the masses of oxygen per nitrogen molecule are half of these amounts, namely, m_o, $2m_o$, $3m_o$, $4m_o$, and $5m_o$. Then for any given mass of nitrogen that contains n nitrogen molecules, the masses of oxygen that can combine with it are nm_o, $2nm_o$, $3nm_o$, $4nm_o$ and $5nm_o$, all of which are whole number multiples of nm_o. That is, the masses conform to the Law of Multiple Proportions.

IV. According to the Dalton theory and molecular formulas that are based on it, 2 atoms of hydrogen combine with 1 atom of oxygen to form a molecule of water; and 2 atoms of chlorine combine with 1 atom of oxygen to form a molecule of chlorine monoxide. That is, 2 atoms of hydrogen and 2 atoms of chlorine combine with the same amount of oxygen. If the mass of a hydrogen atom is m_H, and the mass of a chlorine atom is m_{Cl}, it means that a mass of hydrogen equal to $2m_H$ and a mass of chlorine equal to $2m_{Cl}$ combine with the same amount of oxygen.

According to the Dalton theory, 1 atom of hydrogen combines with 1 atom of chlorine to form a molecule of hydrogen chloride (HCl). That is, a mass of hydrogen equal to m_H combines with a mass of chlorine equal to m_{Cl}. Doubling these amounts we see that a mass of hydrogen equal to $2m_H$ combines with a mass of chlorine equal to $2m_{Cl}$. Thus the Dalton theory and molecular formulas that are based on it explain why the masses of hydrogen and chlorine that combine with the same amount of oxygen also combine with each other; that is, they explain the Law of Equivalent Proportions as it manifests itself in this case.

To derive the Law of Equivalent Proportions in general form as a consequence of Dalton's theory, we argue as follows: Let A, B, and C be three elements such that A and B each combine with C and also combine with each other. Let m_A, m_B, and m_C be the masses of a single atom of each of these elements, respectively. Suppose that under the Dalton theory the reactions in which A combines with C, B combines with C, and A combines with B are given by the following equations:

1) $$x\mathrm{A} + y\mathrm{C} \rightarrow \mathrm{A}_x\mathrm{C}_y,$$

2) $$z\mathrm{B} + w\mathrm{C} \rightarrow \mathrm{B}_z\mathrm{C}_w,$$

3) $$r\mathrm{A} + s\mathrm{B} \rightarrow \mathrm{A}_r\mathrm{B}_s.$$

In order to have the same number of atoms of C in each of the first two reactions, multiply equation 1) by w and equation 2) by y. Then we get

$$wx\mathrm{A} + wy\mathrm{C} \rightarrow w\mathrm{A}_x\mathrm{C}_y, \qquad yz\mathrm{B} + wy\mathrm{C} \rightarrow y\mathrm{B}_z\mathrm{C}_w.$$

That is, wx atoms of A and yz atoms of B combine with the same amount of C (wy atoms of C); or a mass wxm_A of atoms of A and a mass yzm_B of atoms of B combine

28

with the same amount of C (a mass of wym_C of atoms of C). Multiplying equation 3) by $wxyz$, we get

$$wxyzrA + wxyzsB \rightarrow wxyzA_rB_s.$$

Then a mass of A atoms equal to $wxyzrm_A$ combines with a mass of B atoms equal to $wxyzsm_B$. But $wxyzrm_A = yzr(wxm_A)$, and $wxyzsm_B = wxs(yzm_B)$. That is, the masses of A and B that react with each other are simple multiples of the masses of A and B that react with the same amount of C.

V. Assumptions 1 to 4 on page 22 say nothing about how molecules are dispersed in a gas, so they provide no clue to the volumes that different gases may occupy. Consequently assumptions 1 to 4 alone cannot provide an explanation for the Law of Constant Ratios by Volume. Avogadro filled this gap in the Dalton theory in 1811 by adding another assumption, usually referred to as *Avogadro's hypothesis:*

5. Equal volumes of all gases at the same temperature and pressure contain equal numbers of molecules.

To show how assumptions 1 to 5 together successfully explain the Law of Constant Ratios by Volume, let us consider as an example the reaction in which hydrogen combines with oxygen to form water. Suppose that the equation for the reaction is $2H_2 + O_2 \rightarrow 2H_2O$, that is, 2 molecules of hydrogen and 1 molecule of oxygen produce 2 molecules of water. Multiplying by any positive integer n, we see that $2n$ molecules of hydrogen and n molecules of oxygen produce $2n$ molecules of water. Now suppose that, at a given temperature and pressure, n molecules of oxygen occupy a particular volume. Then according to

29

Avogadro's hypothesis, n molecules of hydrogen occupy the same volume, and n molecules of water vapor occupy the same volume. Consequently $2n$ molecules of either will occupy double that volume. This implies that 2 volumes of hydrogen combine with 1 volume of oxygen to produce 2 volumes of vapor. Thus, the Law of Constant Ratios by Volume, as it manifests itself in this reaction, is a consequence of Dalton's theory and Avogadro's hypothesis.

To derive the law in general form, we observe first an immediate consequence of Avogadro's hypothesis. Suppose that at a given temperature and pressure, a unit of volume of gas contains n molecules. Then, by Avogadro's hypothesis, a unit volume of any gas at the same temperature and pressure contains n molecules. Then a volume V_1 of gas contains nV_1 molecules, and a volume V_2 of gas contains nV_2 molecules. Then the ratio of the numbers of molecules contained in volumes V_1 and V_2 respectively is

$$\frac{nV_1}{nV_2} = \frac{V_1}{V_2}.$$

That is, *at the same temperature and pressure, the ratio of the volumes of two gases is the same as the ratio of the numbers of molecules they contain.*

Now, suppose that, in a reaction, x molecules of A combine with y molecules of B to form z molecules of C. Then the ratio of the numbers of molecules of A, B and C in the reaction is $x:y:z$. Consequently, at a fixed temperature and pressure, the ratio of the volumes of A, B and C in the reaction is also $x:y:z$. This observation establishes the Law of Constant Ratios by Volume as a consequence of Dalton's theory and Avogadro's hypothesis.

30

Three Questions

Assumptions 1 to 5 give only the general content of the atomic theory of matter. Since we know now that they successfully explain the five basic laws of chemistry, it is worthwhile to develop the theory in detail. In working out the details of the theory, three fundamental questions must be answered: 1) Given any particular compound or element, what is the mass of one of its molecules? 2) Given any element, what is the mass of one of its atoms? 3) Assuming that we know from the experiments of the chemists what elements are combined in a compound, how many atoms of each element are found in a molecule of the compound? That is, what is the compound's molecular formula? We shall show now how facts determined by experiment and interpreted in the light of the theory provide answers to these questions.

Weighing Molecules

The job of measuring the mass of a molecule is carried out in two steps. The first step is to obtain the relative mass of the molecule, by comparing it with the mass of an oxygen molecule. The second step is to obtain the absolute mass by expressing it in grams.

Atomic Mass Unit

In order to express the relative mass of a molecule, chemists use a special scale of masses in which the mass of an oxygen molecule is arbitrarily assigned the value 32.

31

Then the unit of this scale is $\frac{1}{32}$ of the mass of an oxygen molecule. This unit is called the *atomic mass unit* and is abbreviated as amu. Consequently, by definition of amu, the mass of an oxygen molecule is 32 amu. If we can find out how heavy a molecule is compared to a molecule of oxygen, we can express its mass as a number of amu, and vice versa. Thus, if the mass of a given molecule is $\frac{3}{4}$ the mass of an oxygen molecule, then it is $\frac{3}{4}$ (32 amu) = 24 amu. Conversely, if the mass of a molecule is 24 amu, then it is $\frac{24}{32} = \frac{3}{4}$ times as heavy as an oxygen molecule. The number of amu in the mass of a molecule of an element or a compound is called the *molecular weight* of the element or compound. The number of amu in the mass of an atom of an element is called the *atomic weight* of the element.

Measuring Molecular Weight

We shall consider here only the problem of measuring the molecular weight of a chemical that can be observed in the gaseous state. The method of measurement is based on a simple rule that is easily derived from Avogadro's hypothesis.

Let us consider two different gases which we shall call I and II. Let w_I be the molecular weight of gas I, that is, the mass of one of its molecules, expressed in amu. Let w_{II} be the molecular weight of gas II. Take equal volumes of these gases at the same temperature and pressure. By Avogadro's hypothesis, these equal volumes contain the same number of molecules. Let this number of molecules be n. Let M_I and M_{II} be the masses of these equal volumes of gases I and II, expressed in amu. Then $M_I = nw_I$, and $M_{II} = nw_{II}$. The ratio of these masses is $M_I:M_{II} = nw_I:nw_{II}$, which reduces to $w_I:w_{II}$. In short,

$$(4) \qquad \frac{M_I}{M_{II}} = \frac{w_I}{w_{II}}.$$

That is, *the ratio of the masses of equal volumes of two gases at the same temperature and pressure is the same as the ratio of their molecular weights.*

However, *the ratio of the masses of two substances is the same as the ratio of their weights.* If the weights in grams of the equal volumes of gases I and II that we are considering are W_I and W_{II} respectively, then

$$(5) \qquad \frac{M_I}{M_{II}} = \frac{W_I}{W_{II}}.$$

If we combine equations (4) and (5), we get

$$(6) \qquad \frac{w_I}{w_{II}} = \frac{W_I}{W_{II}}.$$

This gives us a simple rule for comparing the molecular weights of two gases: Simply compare the weights of equal volumes of the two gases at the same conditions of temperature and pressure. If one of the gases is oxygen, this comparison gives the molecular weight of the other in amu. For example, suppose gas I is hydrogen and gas II is oxygen. It is found by experiment that the ratio of the weights of equal volumes of hydrogen and oxygen at the same temperature and pressure is about 1:16. Consequently

$$\frac{w_I}{w_{II}} = \frac{1}{16}, \quad \text{or} \quad w_I = \frac{1}{16}w_{II}, \text{ approximately.}$$

Since w_{II} is the number of amu in the molecular weight of oxygen, which is 32, we have that w_I (the number of amu in the molecular weight of hydrogen) $= \frac{1}{16} (32) = 2$, approximately.

Standard Temperature, Pressure, and Volume

In the procedure described in the preceding paragraph, the experimenter is free to choose any temperature, any pressure, and any volume for the two gases, provided that he chooses the same temperature, pressure and volume for both gases. However, in order to standardize the computations, chemists have agreed to relate all measurements to a particular standard temperature, pressure and volume. As standard temperature they use 0° Celsius, and as standard pressure they use a pressure of 760 millimeters (that is, the pressure that will support a column of 760 millimeters of mercury). The standard volume is defined in this way: Take enough oxygen gas so that the number of grams in its weight is the same as the number of amu in its molecular weight. Then see how large a volume it fills at the standard temperature and pressure. Since the molecular weight of oxygen is 32 amu, the standard volume is the volume at the standard temperature and pressure of 32 grams of oxygen gas. This volume is found by experiment to be 22.4 liters.

To see the significance of this choice of standard volume, let us observe the consequences of using it. In the preceding paragraph, we found that if W_I grams and W_{II} grams are the weights at the same temperature and pressure of equal volumes of two gases whose molecular weights are w_I and w_{II} respectively, then

34

$$\frac{w_I}{w_{II}} = \frac{W_I}{W_{II}}.$$

Now assume that gas II is oxygen, and that we are using the standard temperature and pressure, and the standard volume of 22.4 liters. Then W_{II} = the number of grams in the weight of 22.4 liters of oxygen = 32, and w_{II} = the number of amu in the molecular weight of oxygen = 32. Substituting these values, we obtain

$$\frac{w_I}{32} = \frac{W_I}{32}.$$

Consequently $w_I = W_I$. That is, *the number of amu in the molecular weight of a gas is the same as the number of grams in the weight of 22.4 liters of the gas at the standard temperature and pressure.* For example, if we weigh 22.4 liters of hydrogen gas at the standard temperature and pressure, the weight is found to be 2.016 grams. Therefore the molecular weight of hydrogen is 2.016 amu. If we weigh 22.4 liters of carbon dioxide at the standard temperature and pressure, the weight is found to be about 44 grams. Therefore the molecular weight of carbon dioxide is about 44 amu.

Using Any Temperature, Pressure and Volume

In practice it is not necessary to use a standard volume of a gas at the standard temperature and pressure in order to measure its molecular weight. It suffices to weigh any sample of the gas at any temperature and any pressure. Then from the known weight and volume of the gas at these conditions the molecular weight can be calculated. The calculation is carried out in three steps:

Step I. Use the formula $T_K = T_C + 273$ to convert the Celsius temperature to a Kelvin temperature. (See page 10)

Step II. Use the formula

$$\frac{P_1V_1}{P_2V_2} = \frac{T_1}{T_2}$$

to calculate what the volume of the sample would be at the standard temperature and pressure. (See page 11)

Step III. The weight of a gas at constant temperature and pressure is proportional to its volume. This fact is expressed in the formula

$$\frac{W}{W'} = \frac{V}{V'}.$$

Use this formula to compute the weight of 22.4 liters of the gas at the standard temperature and pressure.

For example, suppose we have a sample of carbon monoxide whose weight is .35 grams, and we find by measurement that its volume is .30 liters when its temperature is 24° Celsius and its pressure is 765 millimeters.

Step I. Find the Kelvin temperature T_K that is equivalent to the Celsius temperature $T_C = 24$.

$$T_K = T_C + 273.$$
$$T_K = 24 + 273 = 297.$$

Step II. Find the volume V_1 that the sample would occupy at standard temperature and pressure ($T_1 = 273$, $P_1 = 760$), if its volume is $V_2 = .30$ liters at a temperature and pressure of $T_2 = 297, P_2 = 765$.

36

$$\frac{P_1 V_1}{P_2 V_2} = \frac{T_1}{T_2}.$$

$$\frac{(760) V_1}{(765)(.30)} = \frac{273}{297}.$$

$$V_1 = \frac{(273)(765)(.30)}{(297)(760)} = .28 \text{ liters.}$$

Step III. Find the weight W at standard temperature and pressure of 22.4 liters of carbon monoxide if .28 liters weigh .35 grams. Use $V = 22.4$, $W' = .35$, $V' = .28$.

$$\frac{W}{W'} = \frac{V}{V'}.$$

$$\frac{W}{.35} = \frac{22.4}{.28}$$

$$W = \frac{(22.4)(.35)}{.28} = 28.$$

That is, a standard volume of 22.4 liters of carbon monoxide at standard conditions of temperature and pressure weighs 28 grams. Therefore the molecular weight of carbon monoxide is 28 amu.

Absolute Mass of a Molecule

The molecular weight of a molecule is the number of amu in its mass. To convert from a mass expressed in amu to a mass expressed in grams it is necessary to know the number of grams there are in one amu. To determine this number, let us think for a moment about the standard volume (22.4 liters) of a gas at standard conditions of temperature and pressure. Let N_0 be the number of molecules it contains. According to Avogadro's hypothesis

37

it is the same number for all gases. The number N_0 is known as *Avogadro's number*. Now suppose that the molecular weight of the gas is w amu. Then the mass of 22.4 liters of the gas is $N_0(w \text{ amu}) = (N_0 w) \times (1 \text{ amu})$. We already know that if the molecular weight of a gas is w amu, then the weight of 22.4 liters of the gas at standard conditions is w grams, and therefore the mass of 22.4 liters of the gas is w grams. Consequently

$$(N_0 w) \times (1 \text{ amu}) = w \text{ grams.}$$

Dividing by $N_0 w$, we find that $1 \text{ amu} = \dfrac{1}{N_0} \text{ gram.}$

There are several ways in which the value of N_0 can be found. We shall see one of these ways in Chapter IV. The value found is $N_0 =$ about 6×10^{23}, that is, 6 followed by 23 zeros, or 600 thousand million million million. Consequently

$$1 \text{ amu} = \frac{1}{N_0} \text{ gram} = \frac{1}{6 \times 10^{23}} \text{ gram} = \frac{10}{6 \times 10^{24}} \text{ gram}$$

$$= \left(\frac{10}{6} \div 10^{24} \right) \text{ gram} = (1.66 \div 10^{24}) \text{ gram}$$

$$= 1.66 \times 10^{-24} \text{ gram,}$$

where, using the customary notation, multiplying by 10^{-24} is understood to mean dividing by 10^{24}, and this, in turn, can be accomplished by moving the decimal point 24 places to the left. That is,

$$1 \text{ amu} = .00000000000000000000000166 \text{ gram.}$$

Now that we know the number of grams in one amu, it is easy to find the mass, in grams, of any molecule, if we know its mass in amu. For example, the mass of an oxygen molecule is 32 amu $= 32 \times 1.66 \times 10^{-24}$ gram $= 5.31 \times 10^{-23}$ gram. The mass of a hydrogen molecule is about 2 amu $= 2 \times 1.66 \times 10^{-24}$ gram $= 3.32 \times 10^{-24}$ gram. The mass of a molecule of carbon dioxide is 44 amu $= 44 \times 1.66 \times 10^{-24}$ gram $= 7.30 \times 10^{-23}$ gram.

Weighing Atoms

It is found by experiment that 1 volume of hydrogen gas combines with 1 volume of chlorine gas to produce 2 volumes of hydrochloric acid gas at the same temperature and pressure. Since 2 volumes of gas contain twice as many molecules as 1 volume of gas at the same temperature and pressure, this means that each molecule of hydrogen gas combines with one molecule of chlorine gas to produce two molecules of hydrochloric acid. Since each molecule of hydrochloric acid contains at least one atom of hydrogen, a molecule of hydrogen must therefore contain at least two atoms of hydrogen. Thus we see that a molecule of an element may contain more than one atom of the element. Consequently the atomic weight of an element need not be the same as the molecular weight of the element. If a molecule of an element contains two atoms, the atomic weight is one half of the molecular weight. If a molecule of an element contains three atoms, the atomic weight is one third of the molecular weight, and so on. This fact is the chief obstacle that stands in the way of determining the atomic weight of an element. In 1860 Cannizzaro showed that there is a simple way of bypassing this obstacle. He pointed out that although a molecule of an element may contain more than one atom of the element, it is likely that there are some compounds of the element whose molecules contain only one atom of the element. The mass contributed by the element to the molecular weight of such a compound would be the atomic weight of the element. Since no compound of an element contains less than one atom of the element, the atomic weight is easily recognized as the smallest mass contributed by the element to the molecular weight of any of its compounds.

For example, chemical analysis shows that chloroform, carbon tetrachloride, hydrogen chloride, sulfur monochloride, and ethyl chloride are all compounds of the element chlorine. The molecular weights of these compounds are shown in the table below:

Compound	Molecular Weight
Chloroform	119 amu
Carbon tetrachloride	154 amu
Hydrogen chloride	36.5 amu
Sulfur monochloride	135 amu
Ethyl chloride	64.5 amu

By quantitative chemical analysis it is possible to find out the percentage of chlorine in each of these compounds. These percentages are found to be 89.10%, 92.19%, 97.24%, 52.51%, and 54.96% respectively. Consequently the mass of chlorine in a chloroform molecule is 89.10% of 119 amu; the mass of chlorine in a carbon tetrachloride molecule is 92.19% of 154 amu; etc. The masses of chlorine computed in this way are shown in this table:

40

Compound	Mass of chlorine in one molecule
Chloroform	89.10% of 119 amu = 106 amu
Carbon tetrachloride	92.19% of 154 amu = 142 amu
Hydrogen chloride	97.24% of 36.5 amu = 35.5 amu
Sulfur monochloride	52.51% of 15 amu = 70.9 amu
Ethyl chloride	54.96% of 64.5 amu = 35.4 amu

Notice that the smallest mass of chlorine in any of these compounds is about 35.4 amu. *Then this must be the approximate mass of one chlorine atom.* Moreover, we can tell from the table how many atoms of chlorine there are in a molecule of each of the compounds listed. A chloroform molecule contains 106 amu = 3 × 35.4 amu of chlorine. Therefore a chloroform molecule contains 3 atoms of chlorine. A carbon tetrachloride molecule contains 142 amu = 4 × 35.4 amu of chlorine. Therefore a carbon tetrachloride molecule contains 4 atoms of chlorine. Similarly, a hydrogen chloride molecule contains 1 atom of chlorine, a sulfur monochloride atom contains 2 atoms of chlorine, and an ethyl chloride molecule contains 1 atom of chlorine.

The molecular weight of chlorine gas is 71.0 amu. Since the atomic weight is about 35.4 amu, it follows that a chlorine molecule contains 2 atoms of chlorine. By similar methods, using the principle of Cannizzaro, it is found that the atomic weight of oxygen is 16 amu. Since the molecular weight of oxygen is 32 amu, a molecule of oxygen contains two atoms of oxygen. The atomic weight of hydrogen is found to be about 1 amu. Since the molecular weight of hydrogen is 2 amu, a molecule of hydrogen contains two hydrogen atoms.

41

Atomic Weight via Specific Heat

Cannizzaro's method can be used to find the atomic weight of any elements whose compounds are easily vaporized. For those elements whose compounds are not easily vaporized, a different method is used, based on measuring the specific heat of the element in the solid state. The specific heat of a substance is the number of calories of heat needed to raise the temperature of one gram of the substance one degree Celsius. In 1819, Dulong and Petit found that for elements whose atomic weights were known, the product of the atomic weight and the specific heat of the solid element is a constant, namely 6.3. Assuming that this rule applies to all elements, the atomic weight of an element can be computed from the formula

$$(7) \qquad \text{atomic weight} = \frac{6.3}{\text{specific heat}}.$$

For example, the specific heat of iron is 0.113 calories per gram. Therefore the atomic weight of iron is about $6.3 \div 0.113 = 56$.

Molecular Formulas

Once we know the molecular weight of a compound, the atomic weight of each element that it contains, and the combining ratios by weight of the elements in the compound, it is easy to figure out the molecular formula for the compound. For example, chemical analysis of the compound called carbon tetrachloride shows that it is a compound of carbon (C) and chlorine (Cl). Quantitative analysis shows that 92.19% of the mass of each molecule of the compound is contributed by chlorine. The balance of the mass, namely $100\% - 92.19\% = 7.81\%$ is contributed by carbon. The molecular weight of carbon tetrachloride is 154 amu. Therefore the mass of chlorine in a carbon tetrachloride molecule is, as we have already seen, 92.19% of 154 amu, or 142 amu; and the mass of carbon in a carbon tetrachloride molecule is 7.81% of 154 amu, or 12 amu. By the method of Cannizzaro it is found that a chlorine atom weighs about 35.4 amu, and a carbon atom weighs about 12 amu. Since 142 is about 4×35.4, and 12 is 1×12, it follows that each molecule of carbon tetrachloride contains 4 atoms of chlorine and 1 atom of carbon. Consequently the molecular formula for carbon tetrachloride is CCl_4.

The molecular formula for water can be determined in the same way. Chemical analysis of water shows that it is a compound of hydrogen (H) and oxygen (O). Quantitative analysis shows that oxygen contributes about 89% of the mass of water, while hydrogen contributes about 11% of the mass. The molecular weight of water is 18 amu, so the mass that oxygen contributes to a single molecule of water is 89% of 18 amu, or about 16 amu, while the mass that hydrogen contributes to a single molecule of water is 11% of 18 amu, or about 2 amu. Since the atomic weight of oxygen is 16, and the atomic weight of hydrogen is about 1, it follows that a molecule of water contains 2 atoms of hydrogen and 1 atom of oxygen. Consequently the molecular formula for water is H_2O.

We have already seen on page 41 that a molecule of

chlorine gas contains 2 atoms of chlorine, a molecule of oxygen gas contains 2 atoms of oxygen, and a molecule of hydrogen gas contains 2 atoms of hydrogen. Consequently the molecular formulas for chlorine, oxygen and hydrogen are Cl_2, O_2, and H_2 respectively.

The Valence of an Element

An important property of an element is the number of atoms of other elements with which it can combine. A numerical measure of this property, called the *valence* of the element, is introduced in the following way: The valence of hydrogen is defined to be 1, and the valence of any other element is defined to be the number of atoms of hydrogen with which an atom of the element combines. For example, since an oxygen atom combines with 2 hydrogen atoms to form a water molecule, the valence of oxygen is 2. Since a chlorine atom combines with 1 hydrogen atom to form a hydrogen chloride molecule, the valence of chlorine is 1. Since a carbon atom combines with 4 hydrogen atoms to form a molecule of methane whose molecular formula is CH_4, the valence of carbon is 4.

When a compound contains only two elements, the numbers of atoms of each element in a molecule of the compound obey this rule: the number of atoms of one element times the valence of that element equals the number of atoms of the other element times the valence of that element. For example, the molecular formula for carbon dioxide is CO_2. There is 1 carbon atom in a molecule of CO_2, and the valence of carbon is 4. The product 1×4 equals 4. There are 2 oxygen atoms in a molecule

44

of CO_2, and the valence of oxygen is 2. The product 2×2 is also 4.

If the atomic weight of an element is divided by its valence, we get its equivalent weight. For example, the atomic weight of oxygen is 16, its valence is 2, and its equivalent weight is $16 \div 2 = 8$. (See page 20)

Some elements have more than one valence. For example, the element iron (Fe) has the valence 2 in some compounds and the valence 3 in other compounds.

Families of Elements

There are some elements that resemble each other in their physical and chemical properties. They tend to combine with the same elements to form similar compounds, and they have the same valences in these compounds. The elements that resemble each other are classified together in groups or families of elements. For example, lithium (Li), sodium (Na), and potassium (K) are members of the family of *alkali metals*. Fluorine (F), chlorine (Cl), bromine (Br), and iodine (I), are members of the *halogen* family of non-metals. Helium (He), neon (Ne), argon (Ar), and krypton (Kr) are members of the family of *noble* gases. The alkali metals and the halogens are very active chemically, that is, they react easily with many other elements to form compounds. The noble gases, on the other hand, are very inactive chemically. They form almost no compounds at all.

The Periodic Table of the Elements

In 1869 Meyer and Mendeleyev, working independently, made an important discovery about the chemical

45

elements. They found that if the elements are listed in order of increasing atomic weight, elements that are in the same family occur at regular intervals in the list. In this respect the list of elements resembles a list of the days of a month. The days of a month are classified into families by the day of the week on which each day of the month falls. Thus, some of the days of the month are Sundays, some are Mondays, and so on. If the days of a month are listed in order of increasing date, days that belong to the same family occur at regular intervals in the list. For example, if the 1st of the month is a Sunday, so are the 8th, the 15th, the 22nd, and the 29th. To describe this property of the list of days of a month we say that the days of the week occur *periodically* in the list. Because of this periodic property of the list we can list the days of a month in a table in which, while the numbers

January			1964			
S	M	T	W	T	F	S
			1	2	3	4
5	6	7	8	9	10	11
12	13	14	15	16	17	18
19	20	21	22	23	24	25
26	27	28	29	30	31	

A page of a calendar is a periodic table of the days of a month.

designating the days of the month increase from left to right in each line, and from top to bottom line by line, the days that fall on the same weekday fall under each other in the same vertical column. This arrangement,

46

used in the calendar, is called a *periodic table*. Similarly the chemical elements can be arranged in a periodic table, in which, while the atomic weights of the elements increase from left to right in each line, and from top to bottom line by line, the elements that belong to the same family fall under each other in the same vertical column. A modern version of the periodic table of the elements is shown on page 48.

There were three imperfections in the original periodic table of the elements. 1) In order to keep elements of the same family in the same vertical column it was necessary to leave some gaps in the table. For example, there was a gap in the 21st place, right after calcium. 2) To keep the families in vertical columns it was sometimes necessary to depart from the order of increasing atomic weight. For example, the cobalt atom has a higher atomic weight than the nickel atom, but it is listed before the nickel atom in the table. 3) Some elements didn't fit well into the table at all, but had to be listed separately. This was true of the entire family of elements called the *rare earths,* or the *lanthanide series.*

The discovery of the periodic table raised two very challenging questions: 1) What accounts for the near-perfection of the table, as a result of which chemical families occur periodically in the list of elements tabulated by atomic weight? 2) What accounts for the imperfections in the table? Part of the second question was answered immediately by Mendeleyev. He guessed that the gaps in the table represented elements that had not yet been discovered. As these unknown elements were discovered one by one, the gaps were filled. The 21st place, for example, is now filled by the element *scandium.* The

PERIODIC TABLE OF THE ELEMENTS

I	II	III	IV	V	VI	VII	VIII			0
1 H 1.008										2 He 4.003
3 Li 6.940	4 Be 9.013	5 B 10.82	6 C 12.011	7 N 14.008	8 O 16.000	9 F 19.00				10 Ne 20.183
11 Na 22.991	12 Mg 24.32	13 Al 26.98	14 Si 28.09	15 P 30.975	16 S 32.066	17 Cl 35.457				18 Ar 39.944
19 K 39.100	20 Ca 40.08	21 Sc 44.96	22 Ti 47.90	23 V 50.95	24 Cr 52.01	25 Mn 54.94	26 Fe 55.85	27 Co 58.94	28 Ni 58.71	
29 Cu 63.54	30 Zn 65.38	31 Ga 69.72	32 Ge 72.60	33 As 74.91	34 Se 78.96	35 Br 79.916				36 Kr 83.80
37 Rb 85.48	38 Sr 87.63	39 Y 88.92	40 Zr 91.22	41 Nb 92.91	42 Mo 95.95	43 Tc (98)	44 Ru 101.10	45 Rh 102.91	46 Pd 106.4	
47 Ag 107.880	48 Cd 112.41	49 In 114.82	50 Sn 118.70	51 Sb 121.76	52 Te 127.61	53 I 126.91				54 Xe 131.30
55 Cs 132.91	56 Ba 137.36	57-71 La series*	72 Hf 178.50	73 Ta 180.95	74 W 183.86	75 Re 186.22	76 Os 190.2	77 Ir 192.2	78 Pt 195.09	
79 Au 197.0	80 Hg 200.61	81 Tl 204.39	82 Pb 207.21	83 Bi 209.00	84 Po (210)	85 At (210)				86 Rn (222)
87 Fr (223)	88 Ra 226.05	89-103 Ac series**								

* Lanthanide series:	57 La 138.92	58 Ce 140.13	59 Pr 140.92	60 Nd 144.27	61 Pm (147)	62 Sm 150.35	63 Eu 152.0	64 Gd 157.26	65 Tb 158.93	66 Dy 162.51	67 Ho 164.94	68 Er 167.27	69 Tm 168.94	70 Yb 173.04	71 Lu 174.99
** Actinide series:	89 Ac (227)	90 Th 232.05	91 Pa (231)	92 U 238.07	93 Np (237)	94 Pu (242)	95 Am (243)	96 Cm (247)	97 Bk (247)	98 Cf (251)	99 Es (254)	100 Fm (253)	101 Md (256)	102 No (254)	103 Lw (257)

Atomic Number
Atomic Symbol
Atomic Weight

Numbers in parentheses show mass number of most stable known isotope (see page 88)

48

answers to the first question and the rest of the second question are supplied by the modern theory of atomic structure. In the remainder of this book we outline the development of this theory. In Chapter VII we shall see how the theory successfully explains the periodic table and its imperfections.

The number of the place that an element occupies in the periodic table is called its *atomic number* and is usually designated by the letter Z. For hydrogen, $Z = 1$, for helium, $Z = 2$, for lithium $Z = 3$, and so on. The significance of the atomic number in the theory of atomic structure is discussed in Chapter IV.

III

Motion, Electricity and Light

THE chemists discovered the atom, but the physicists analysed its structure. In this chapter we present some physical concepts and relationships that play a part in the analysis. All measurements used will be expressed in the centimeter-gram-second system of measurements. It will be understood then, when units are not mentioned explicitly, that distances are measured in centimeters, masses are measured in grams, time is measured in seconds, forces are measured in dynes, energy is measured in ergs, etc.

Velocity

A weather report on wind conditions always gives the speed of the wind and its direction. It may say, for example, that the wind is from the west with a speed of 10 miles per hour. The combination of speed and direction of motion is known as *velocity*. A velocity can be represented graphically by an arrow. The direction in which the arrow points shows the direction of motion, and the length of the arrow shows the speed of the motion.

If a body moves through a distance s in a time interval

t, its average speed v in that interval is given by the formula

$$(8) \qquad v = \frac{s}{t}.$$

If the speed does not change during the interval, this formula also gives the exact speed at each instant in the interval.

If a body, after moving for a length of time t, continues to move for an additional small amount of time, it is customary to represent this small increment in time by the symbol Δt, read as "delta t," and understood to mean "the change in t." If s represents the distance the body has moved in the time t, it is customary to write Δs for the additional distance that it moves during the time interval Δt. The symbol Δs is read as "delta s," and is understood to mean "the change in s." By formula (8), the average speed during the time interval Δt is

$$(9) \qquad v = \frac{\Delta s}{\Delta t}.$$

If we multiply both side of equation (9) by Δt, we get

$$(10) \qquad \Delta s = v(\Delta t).$$

Momentum

A moving body tends to keep moving. There is a measure of this persistence of motion called the *momentum* of the body. If a body with mass m has a speed v, and momentum M, these quantities are related by the formula

$$(11) \qquad M = mv.$$

52

Changing Velocity

The velocity of a moving body may change in three ways: the speed of motion may change, the direction of motion may change, or both may change. If the speed is changing, it is possible to make an estimate of the speed at a particular instant in this way: find the distance Δs that the body moves during a small interval of time Δt starting with that instant. Then equation (9) gives an approximate value of the speed at that instant. The smaller the interval of time Δt is, the better the approximation is. The exact value of the speed at that instant is the limit approached by these approximate values as Δt approaches zero.

A change in velocity, like the velocity itself, has both a magnitude and a direction, and can be represented by an arrow. When a velocity and a change in the velocity are known, the new velocity that results can be found graphically by following this simple rule: Draw an arrow to represent the original velocity. From the head of this arrow draw an arrow to represent the change of velocity. Then the new velocity is represented by an arrow drawn from the tail of the first arrow to the head of the second arrow, as shown in the diagram below. The diagram also shows how to find the change in velocity, if both the old velocity and the new velocity are known: Draw the ar-

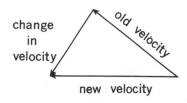

change
in
velocity

old velocity

new velocity

rows that represent the old and the new velocities so that their tails are at the same point. Then the change in velocity is represented by the arrow drawn from the head of the old velocity to the head of the new velocity.

Let v be the speed of a moving body (the magnitude of its velocity), and let Δv be the magnitude of the change in velocity that takes place in a time interval Δt. The average rate of change of the velocity is called the average *acceleration a,* and is given by the formula

$$(12) \qquad\qquad a = \frac{\Delta v}{\Delta t}.$$

If the acceleration does not change during the interval, this formula also gives the exact acceleration at each instant in the interval. If the acceleration does change, the formula gives an approximation of the acceleration at a particular instant if we use as Δt a small interval that begins with that instant. The smaller the interval is, the better the approximation is. The exact value of the acceleration at that instant is the limit approached by these approximate values as Δt approaches zero. If we multiply both sides of equation (12) by Δt, we get a formula for the approximate magnitude of the change in velocity, Δv, during a small interval of time Δt, in terms of the acceleration a at the start of the interval:

$$(13) \qquad\qquad \Delta v = a(\Delta t).$$

Force

A force is a push or a pull. When a force acts on a body that is free to move, it changes the motion of the body.

54

The magnitude of the force F, the mass m of the body, and the acceleration a caused by the force are related by the equation

$$(14) \qquad\qquad F = ma.$$

If the values of F and m are unchanging, or constant, then the value of a is constant.

Electrical Charges

There are two kinds of electrical charges, positive and negative. Electrical charges may be measured in terms of units called electrostatic units (esu). The measure of a charge is a positive number if the charge is positive, and it is a negative number if the charge is negative. If a body has a charge a, and another charge b is placed on it, the total charge becomes $a + b$, where the addition is done as in elementary algebra. For example, if a charge of -3 is added to a charge of 2, the total charge becomes $2 + (-3) = -1$. If a charge of -6 is added to a charge of 6, the total charge becomes $6 + (-6) = 0$. When the charge on a body is 0, we say that the body is *electrically neutral*. If a charge is removed from a body, the charge that remains can be calculated by subtraction. For example, if a charge of -3 is removed from a body that is electrically neutral, the remaining charge is $0 - (-3) = 3$.

Any two electrical charges exert a force on each other. If the charges are of the same kind, the force between them is a force of repulsion. If the charges are of opposite kinds, the force is a force of attraction. If each of two charges is concentrated at a separate point, if the distance between the points is r, and the charges, measured in electrostatic units, are Q and q respectively, then the force between them is given by the formula

(15) $$F = \frac{Qq}{r^2}.$$

If an electrical charge moves across a magnetic field, the field exerts a force on the charge, tending to deflect it from its path. The field strength may be represented by an arrow. If the initial velocity of the moving charge is perpendicular to the field, the force exerted on the charge is perpendicular to both the magnetic field and the velocity of the charge. Then the charge moves in a circle

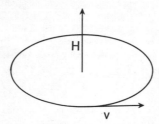

whose plane is perpendicular to the magnetic field. If the strength of the magnetic field is H, if the magnitude of the charge is e, and its speed is v, then the magnitude of the force exerted on the charge is

(16) $$F = e\frac{v}{c}H,$$

where c is the speed of light. The direction of the force is toward the center of the circle.

56

Work

A force is capable of doing work. It does work when it pushes an object from one place to another. If a constant force with magnitude F pushes an object through a distance Δs in the direction of the force, the amount of work W that is done is defined by the equation

$$(17) \qquad W = F(\Delta s).$$

If the force is not constant but its magnitude is always close to some value F as it acts through the distance Δs, then equation (17) gives an approximate value of the work done. If the force changes considerably as it acts, we can get an approximate value of the work done in this way: Divide the distance Δs into n segments $(\Delta s)_1$, $(\Delta s)_2, \ldots, (\Delta s)_n$. Make the lengths of the segments small enough so that the force does not change much as the body moves through one of these segments. Let F_1 be one of the values of the force as it acts through the distance $(\Delta s)_1$, let F_2 be one of the values of the force as it acts through the distance $(\Delta s)_2$, etc. Then an approximate value of the work done as the force acts through the total distance is given by

$$(18) \qquad W_n = F_1(\Delta s)_1 + F_2(\Delta s)_2 + \cdots + F_n(\Delta s)_n.$$

We can get better and better approximations to the value of the work done by dividing the distance into more and more segments with smaller and smaller lengths. The exact value W of the work done is the limit approached by these approximations as the number of segments is increased to infinity while their maximum length is decreased to zero.

Kinetic Energy

A moving body is also capable of doing work. The work that it can do by virtue of its motion is called its *kinetic energy*. If a body that is initially at rest is pushed into motion by a force, the energy of the work done by the force is transformed into the kinetic energy of the body. We can use this fact to derive a formula for kinetic energy. Suppose that a constant force F, acting on a body with mass m, pushes it through a distance Δs in an interval of time Δt. Let the acceleration imparted to the body be a. Then the value of a is constant. Assume that the body's initial speed is 0, and that its final speed is v. Then the magnitude of the change in velocity, $\Delta v = v$. By equation (17), the work done, $W = F(\Delta s)$. Let $\bar{v}$ (read as "v bar") be the average speed of the body during the interval Δt. By equation (10) on page 52, $\Delta s = \bar{v}(\Delta t)$, and by equation (14) on page 55, $F = ma$. Substituting these values of Δs and F into equation (17), we get

$$(19) \qquad W = ma\bar{v}(\Delta t) = m\bar{v}[a(\Delta t)].$$

By equation (13) on page 54, $a(\Delta t) = \Delta v$, which in this case equals v. Moreover, since the value of a is constant, $\bar{v}$, the average speed, is the average of the initial and final speed, that is, $\bar{v} = \frac{1}{2}(0 + v) = \frac{1}{2}v$. Making these substitutions in equation (19), we get

$$(20) \qquad W = m(\tfrac{1}{2}v)v = \tfrac{1}{2}mv^2.$$

Since the kinetic energy stored in the body when its speed is v is equal to the work that was done to give it that speed, we have, finally,

$$(21) \qquad \text{Kinetic energy} = \tfrac{1}{2}mv^2.$$

Potential Energy

An electrical charge Q tends to push or pull any other charge that is near it. To describe this fact we say that the charge is surrounded by a field of electrostatic force. Any charge q that is in this field of force is subjected to either a push or a pull. Since the push or pull can make it move, and, as it moves, it can do work, the charge q is capable of doing work because of its position in the electrostatic field of force. The work that it can do by virtue of its position in the electrostatic field of force is called its (electrostatic) *potential energy*. Specifically, if q is at a distance r from Q, we define the *potential energy* of q to be the work done by the force exerted by Q on q as q moves away to an infinite distance from Q. To obtain a formula for the potential energy of q, we shall first calculate the work done as q moves from the distance r to a greater but finite distance R. We shall designate this amount of work by the symbol $W(r, R)$. Then the potential energy of q at a distance r from Q will be the limit of $W(r, R)$ as R becomes infinite.

The electrostatic force between Q and q when the distance between them is r is given by formula (15), namely,

$$F = \frac{Qq}{r^2}.$$

In the special case where $Q = q = 1$, the formula becomes

$$F = \frac{1}{r^2}.$$

Notice that the force in the general formula is simply Qq times the force that occurs in this special case. To derive the formula for the potential energy, we shall derive it first for the special case only. Then the general formula can be obtained easily from the special case by simply multiplying the force, wherever it occurs in the computation, by Qq.

For simplicity, we shall assume that the charge q moves away from Q in a straight line. In the diagram below, points on the straight line are designated by their distances from Q. Thus, the point labeled 0 is the point where Q is located. The point labeled r is the point at a distance r from Q. The point labeled R is the point at a distance R from Q.

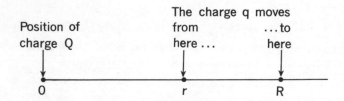

Assume $Q = q = 1$. As q moves from r to R, the force acting on it changes from $1/r^2$ to $1/R^2$. To calculate the work done, we follow the procedure outlined on page 57. We shall divide the distance between r and R into n equal segments, and use formula (18) to find an approximation W_n to the value of the work done. Then we shall find the exact value $W(r, R)$ of the work done by finding the limit of W_n as n becomes infinite.

Let us begin by choosing $n = 1$ to get a very crude approximation, $W_1 = F_1(\Delta s)_1$, where F_1 is a value that F takes on as the charge moves from point r to R, and where $(\Delta s)_1$ is the distance from r to R. The distance

60

$(\Delta s)_1$ is equal to $R - r$. The force F_1 may be chosen as any value between $1/r^2$ (the value of F at r), and $1/R^2$ (the value of F at R). We shall make a choice of F_1 that will enable us to put the formula for W_1 in a simple form. We note first that, by our assumptions, $r < R$. If we multiply both sides of this inequality by r, we get $r^2 < rR$. If, on the other hand, we multiply both sides by R, we get $rR < R^2$. Combining these last two inequalities, we get $r^2 < rR < R^2$. That is, of the three numbers r^2, R^2, and rR, r^2 is the smallest, R^2 is the largest, and rR is between the two extremes. Now we shall compare the reciprocals of these three numbers, namely $1/r^2$, $1/R^2$, and $1/rR$. The larger a number is, the smaller its reciprocal is. Consequently $1/R^2 < 1/rR < 1/r^2$. That is, the number $1/rR$ is between the numbers $1/r^2$ and $1/R^2$. Now, as q moves from r to R, the value of F changes gradually from $1/r^2$ to $1/R^2$. In the course of this gradual change, it passes through every value between $1/r^2$ and $1/R^2$. Since $1/rR$ is between these numbers, F takes on the value $1/rR$ at some point in the segment from r to R. We take this value as our choice of F_1. Then, substituting $R - r$ for $(\Delta s)_1$, and $1/rR$ for F_1, we have

$$(22) \qquad W_1 = \frac{1}{rR} (R - r) = \frac{R - r}{rR}.$$

However, $\dfrac{R - r}{rR} = \dfrac{1}{r} - \dfrac{1}{R}$, as can be verified by using

the rules for the addition and subtraction of fractions. Consequently, we have

$$(23) \qquad W_1 = \frac{1}{r} - \frac{1}{R}.$$

61

Now we make a similar computation for W_n with choices of n that are greater than 1. As a specific example of how the computation goes, let us first take $n = 4$. Then the segment from r to R is being divided into 4 equal parts. In the diagram below, r is designated by r_1, R is

$$0 \qquad r = r_1 \quad r_2 \quad r_3 \quad r_4 \quad r_5 = R$$

designated by r_5, and the points of division between them are r_2, r_3, and r_4. By equation (18), we have

(24) $\qquad W_4 = F_1(\Delta s)_1 + F_2(\Delta s)_2 + F_3(\Delta s)_3 + F_4(\Delta s)_4,$

where $(\Delta s)_1 =$ the distance from r_1 to $r_2 = r_2 - r_1,$
$\qquad (\Delta s)_2 =$ the distance from r_2 to $r_3 = r_3 - r_2,$
$\qquad (\Delta s)_3 =$ the distance from r_3 to $r_4 = r_4 - r_3,$
$\qquad (\Delta s)_4 =$ the distance from r_4 to $r_5 = r_5 - r_4.$

An argument like the one used above shows that $r_1{}^2 < r_1 r_2 < r_2{}^2$, and therefore $1/r_2{}^2 < 1/r_1 r_2 < 1/r_1{}^2$. That is, the number $1/r_1 r_2$ lies between the numbers $1/r_1{}^2$ and $1/r_2{}^2$. The force F has the value $1/r_1{}^2$ at the point r_1, and it has the value $1/r_2{}^2$ at the point r_2. Consequently, somewhere in the segment between r_1 and r_2 the force F takes on the value $1/r_1 r_2$. We therefore choose $F_1 = 1/r_1 r_2$. Similarly, somewhere in the segment between r_2 and r_3 the force F takes on the value $1/r_2 r_3$, so we choose $F_2 = 1/r_2 r_3$; somewhere in the segment between r_3 and r_4 the force F takes on the value $1/r_3 r_4$, so we choose $F_3 = 1/r_3 r_4$; somewhere in the segment between r_4 and r_5 the force F takes on the value $1/r_4 r_5$, so we choose $F_4 = 1/r_4 r_5$. Making all these substitutions into equation (24), we get

62

$$(25) \quad W_4 = \frac{r_2 - r_1}{r_1 r_2} + \frac{r_3 - r_2}{r_2 r_3} + \frac{r_4 - r_3}{r_3 r_4} + \frac{r_5 - r_4}{r_4 r_5}.$$

But $\quad \dfrac{r_2 - r_1}{r_1 r_2} = \dfrac{1}{r_1} - \dfrac{1}{r_2}, \qquad \dfrac{r_3 - r_2}{r_2 r_3} = \dfrac{1}{r_2} - \dfrac{1}{r_3},$

$$\frac{r_4 - r_3}{r_3 r_4} = \frac{1}{r_3} - \frac{1}{r_4}, \quad \text{and} \quad \frac{r_5 - r_4}{r_4 r_5} = \frac{1}{r_4} - \frac{1}{r_5}.$$

Making these substitutions into equation (25), we get

$$(26) \quad W_4 = \frac{1}{r_1} - \frac{1}{r_2} + \frac{1}{r_2} - \frac{1}{r_3} + \frac{1}{r_3} - \frac{1}{r_4} + \frac{1}{r_4} - \frac{1}{r_5}.$$

All terms on the right-hand side of this equation cancel except the first term and the last term. So

$$(27) \quad W_4 = \frac{1}{r_1} - \frac{1}{r_5}.$$

But r_1 stands for r, and r_5 stands for R. Consequently

$$(28) \quad W_4 = \frac{1}{r} - \frac{1}{R}.$$

The procedure used when $n = 4$ may be used when n is any positive integer. We designate the point r by r_1 and the point R by r_{n+1}, and we insert between them the points $r_2, \ldots, r_n$ to divide the segment between r and R into n equal parts. We choose $F_1 = 1/r_1 r_2$, $F_2 = 1/r_2 r_3, \ldots$, $F_n = 1/r_n r_{n+1}$. Moreover, $(\Delta s)_1 = r_2 - r_1$, $(\Delta s)_2 = r_3 - r_2$, $\ldots, (\Delta s)_n = r_{n+1} - r_n$. Then,

$$(29) \quad W_n = F_1 (\Delta s)_1 + F_2 (\Delta s)_2 + \cdots + F_n (\Delta s)_n$$

$$= \frac{r_2 - r_1}{r_1 r_2} + \frac{r_3 - r_2}{r_2 r_3} + \cdots + \frac{r_{n+1} - r_n}{r_n r_{n+1}}$$

$$= \frac{1}{r_1} - \frac{1}{r_2} + \frac{1}{r_2} - \frac{1}{r_3} + \cdots + \frac{1}{r_n} - \frac{1}{r_{n+1}}$$

$$= \frac{1}{r_1} - \frac{1}{r_{n+1}} = \frac{1}{r} - \frac{1}{R}.$$

Notice that W_n has the same value for all values of n. Since W_n does not change in value as n becomes infinite, the limit of W_n as n becomes infinite is this same value. That is,

(30) $W(r, R) =$ the limit of W_n as n becomes infinite

$$= \frac{1}{r} - \frac{1}{R}.$$

This is the value of $W(r, R)$ in the special case where $Q = q = 1$. To obtain a general formula for $W(r, R)$, we multiply each force $F_1, F_2, \ldots, F_n$ used above by Qq. This multiplies by Qq every term in the expression for W_n in equation (29), and hence multiplies the value of W_n by Qq. Thus we obtain the general formulas

(31) $$W_n = \frac{Qq}{r} - \frac{Qq}{R}, \quad \text{and}$$

(32) $$W(r, R) = \frac{Qq}{r} - \frac{Qq}{R}.$$

Now, to get the potential energy of q at a distance r from Q, we find the limit of $W(r, R)$ as R becomes infinite. As R becomes infinite, the fraction Qq/R becomes smaller and smaller and approaches zero as a limit. Therefore the limit of $W(r, R)$ as R becomes infinite is $(Qq/r) - O = Qq/r$. Consequently we have this formula for the potential energy of the charge q at a distance r from the charge Q:

(33)   Potential energy $= \dfrac{Qq}{r}.$

Uniform Circular Motion

Suppose a small body with mass m is moving counter-clockwise around the circle of radius r whose center is the

64

point O, shown in the diagram below. Suppose, too, that the speed of the body as it moves around the circle has the constant value v. That is, in every second the body moves a distance of v centimeters of arc along the circum-

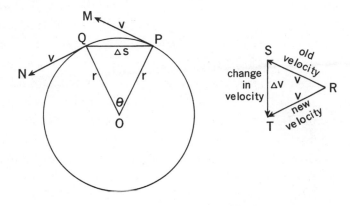

ference of the circle. Then the motion of the body is said to be *uniform circular motion*. When the moving body is at the point P, its direction of motion is along the line tangent to the circle at P. So the velocity of the body when it is at P may be represented by an arrow of length v that is tangent to the circle at P. After a small interval of time Δt the body will have moved a distance Δs around the circle to the point Q. Its velocity at Q may be represented by an arrow of length v that is tangent to the circle at Q. Notice that while the velocities at the points P and Q have the same magnitude, they do not have the same direction. Therefore these two velocities are not the same. So, in its passage from P to Q the velocity of the body has changed. Therefore the acceleration of the body, the rate of change of its velocity, is not zero. We shall derive a formula for the acceleration a of the body.

65

First we determine graphically the change in velocity that occurs when the body moves from P to Q. To do so we draw from the same point R an arrow RS to represent the old velocity (which the body has at P), and an arrow RT to represent the new velocity (which the body has at Q). The lengths of both arrows are equal to v. The arrow ST represents the change in velocity. The length of ST is Δv, the magnitude of the change in velocity. Now we invoke some elementary geometry to compare triangle RST with triangle OPQ. The tangent PM is perpendicular to the radius OP, so we may think of it as being rigidly attached to the radius at right angles to it. As the body moves from P to Q, the rigid configuration of the radius to the body and the tangent at the end of the radius moves with it. That is, the L-shaped figure OPM moves to the new position OQN. In the course of this motion the radius turns through an angle POQ. Let the number of degrees in this angle be θ. Since the tangent is rigidly attached to the moving radius, the tangent also turns through the same number of degrees. The angle through which the tangent line turns is represented in the diagram by angle SRT. Consequently angle SRT also contains θ degrees. In triangle POQ, both PO and QO have length r. Therefore triangle POQ is isosceles, and the base angles QPO and OPQ are equal. The number of degrees in each of them is therefore $\frac{1}{2}(180 - \theta)$. However, triangle SRT is also isosceles, since RS and RT both have length v. Therefore the base angles of triangle SRT are also equal, and the number of degrees in each of them is $\frac{1}{2}(180 - \theta)$. Consequently the three angles of triangle POQ and the three angles of triangle SRT are respectively equal. Therefore the triangles are similar, and their correspond-

66

ing sides are proportional. In particular, we have the proportion

$$\frac{ST}{SR} = \frac{QP}{PO}.$$

The length of ST is Δv. The length of SR is v. The length of PO is r. The length of the chord QP is approximately equal to the length of the arc QP, which is Δs. Making these substitutions, we get the approximate equation

$$\frac{\Delta v}{v} = \frac{\Delta s}{r}.$$

By equation (10) on page 52, $\Delta s = v(\Delta t)$. Making this substitution, we get

$$\frac{\Delta v}{v} = \frac{v}{r}\,(\Delta t).$$

Solving this equation for Δv, we get,

$$\Delta v = \frac{v^2}{r}\,(\Delta t).$$

Then, dividing by Δt, we get

$$\frac{\Delta v}{\Delta t} = \frac{v^2}{r}.$$

This is only an approximate equation, because we obtained it by using an approximate value for the length of the chord QP. However, it becomes more and more exact as Δt approaches zero. But the limiting value of $\frac{\Delta v}{\Delta t}$ as Δt approaches zero is precisely what we call the acceleration a. (See page 54) Therefore

(34) $$a = \frac{v^2}{r}.$$

Wherever there is an acceleration that is not zero, there must be a force that accounts for the acceleration. This force, which keeps the body moving in a circle, is called the *centripetal force*. The magnitude of the force is given by equation (14): $F = ma$. If we substitute for a the value given by equation (34), we get this formula for the centripetal force:

$$(35) \qquad F = \frac{mv^2}{r}.$$

Angular Momentum

A spinning body tends to keep spinning. There is a measure of this persistence of spinning motion called *angular momentum*. When a body moves along the circumference of a circle, it is as though the circle were spinning around its center and carrying the body with it as it spins. Consequently there is an angular momentum associated with circular motion. If the body has momentum M, and the radius of the circle is r, the angular momentum p is given by the formula

$$(36) \qquad p = Mr.$$

According to equation (11), $M = mv$. Substituting this value of M into equation (36), we get

$$(37) \qquad p = mvr.$$

Light Waves

Light is a form of energy that is radiated through space in waves. The waves may be represented diagrammati-

68

cally by a sinuous line like the one shown below. The distance between consecutive crests in a wave is called a wavelength, and is represented by the Greek letter λ (lambda). Sunlight is a mixture of light of different

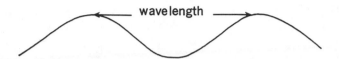

colors. In a rainbow, the colors are separated and arranged side by side. Each distinct color in a rainbow has a different wavelength. The wavelength λ of light of a single color (monochromatic light) can be measured in the following way: A beam of monochromatic light diverging from a light source S is allowed to pass through a lens L and then two narrow slits that are separated by a small distance d on a screen R. The lens is placed so that it bends the diverging rays of light and makes them parallel. On the other side of the screen each slit becomes a separate source of diverging rays of light. These rays of light are caught on a second screen T. (See diagram I) In this way each illuminated point on the screen T receives two rays of light, one from each slit. These two rays may have traveled along paths of different lengths, as shown in diagram II. Where the difference between the path lengths is $n\lambda$, where n is an integer, then the wave-trains in the two rays are in step. That is, crest coincides with crest, and trough coincides with trough. Then the waves reenforce each other, and the point where they fall on T is brightly illuminated. Where the difference between the path lengths is $(n + \frac{1}{2})\lambda$, the wave-trains in the two rays are out of step. That is, crest coincides with trough and

69

trough coincides with crest. Then the waves interfere with each other, or cancel each other, and the point where they fall on T is not illuminated at all. As a result, there is a series of alternating light and dark bands on the screen T. These bands are called *interference* bands. The effect is as though the screen R splits the beam that crosses it into

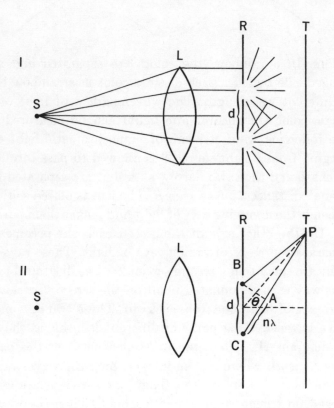

many separate beams, each turned through a different angle from the direction of the original beam. Diagram II above shows one of these beams turned through an angle θ, to form a bright band at P on screen T. The sides of angle ABC are respectively perpendicular to the sides of θ, and therefore angle $ABC = \theta$. Then $\sin \theta = \sin ABC = n\lambda/d$, where $n\lambda$ is the difference in length of the paths followed by the rays from the two slits on their way to P. The smallest angle θ through which a beam is turned occurs when $n = 1$. For this case $\sin \theta = \lambda/d$. Multiplying both sides of this equation by d, we find that $\lambda = d \sin \theta$. Since both d and θ can be measured, this formula allows us to compute the wavelength λ.

A similar separation of a beam of monochromatic light into many divergent beams can be effected if the screen R has many slits instead of only two. Such a screen with many slits is called a *diffraction grating*. If a mixture of colors is passed through a diffraction grating, the smallest angle through which each different color is turned varies with its wavelength. As a result, the colors are separated to form a spectrum on the screen T where monochromatic light forms only a single bright band. The wavelength of each color in the spectrum can be calculated from the formula $\lambda = d \sin \theta$, where θ is the angle through which that particular color was turned.

Light waves travel at a speed of 3×10^{10} centimeters per second. This speed is usually represented by the symbol c. When monochromatic light moves through space, the number of waves that pass a fixed point in a second is called the frequency of the wave. We shall designate the frequency by the symbol f. If f waves pass a point in a second, and each wave has length λ, then $f\lambda$ is the distance that the wave advances in a second. But the distance it advances per second is its speed c. Therefore f, λ, and c are related by the equation

(38) $$f\lambda = c.$$

Monochromatic light can be identified by specifying either its wavelength or its frequency. It can also be identified by its wave number, the number of waves in 1 centimeter, usually designated by the Greek letter ν (nu). Since the length of one wave is λ, the number of waves in 1 centimeter is $1/\lambda$. From equation (38) we find that $1/\lambda = f/c$. Consequently we have this formula for the wave number:

$$(39) \qquad \nu = \frac{1}{\lambda} = \frac{f}{c}, \quad \text{or} \quad c\nu = f.$$

Electromagnetic Waves

An oscillating electric current produces electromagnetic waves that radiate through space with the speed of light. Radio waves are examples of these electromagnetic waves. It is now understood that light is also electromagnetic radiation, differing from radio waves in wavelength and frequency. Electromagnetic waves from the shortest to

wavelength

3×10^{-10}	3×10^{-8}	3×10^{-6}	visible light 3×10^{-4}	.03	.3	3×10^{2}	3×10^{4}	3×10^{6}
gamma waves	x-rays	ultraviolet	infrared		microwaves		long radio waves	

The spectrum of electromagnetic radiation
(wavelength is in centimeters)

the longest ones known are now classified into families in order of increasing wavelength as follows: gamma rays, X rays, ultraviolet rays, visible light, infrared rays, microwaves, and radio waves. The spectrum of electromagnetic radiation is shown in the diagram on page 72.

IV

Electricity in the Atom

Electrons in the Atom

A TELEVISION picture tube is a modern version of a cathode ray tube, whose interesting properties were first studied over a hundred years ago. A cathode ray tube is a glass tube enclosing a gas whose pressure has been reduced to below one thousandth of a millimeter. There are two electrodes in the tube to which a source of high voltage is attached. The negative electrode is called the *cathode*. The positive electrode is called the *anode*. If the voltage is high enough, rays known as cathode rays emanate from the cathode. When the rays strike the glass wall of the tube opposite the cathode, the glass glows with a fluorescent light. Laboratory studies of cathode rays showed that they have the following properties: 1) the rays normally travel in straight lines; 2) they can be deflected by electrostatic fields or magnetic fields; 3) their behavior is independent of the chemical composition of the cathode or the gas that is enclosed in the tube. Properties 1) and 2) can be explained by the assumption that the rays are streams of small charged particles. The direction in which the rays are deflected by an electrostatic or a magnetic field requires that the

75

charges on the particles be negative. Property 3) indicates that these particles are constituents of all matter. The particles in a cathode ray are now known as *electrons*. So the basic assumption made to explain the behavior of cathode rays may be expressed in these words: *Every atom contains small negatively charged particles called electrons.*

Let $-e$ be the charge on a single electron. Let m be the mass of the electron. We outline now the procedure by which these quantities have been measured.

Measuring e/m

The first step toward measuring e and m is to measure their ratio. This was first done by Thomson in 1894. There are many ways of determining the ratio e/m. We shall outline one method in which the mathematical reasoning is easy to follow.

Step I: In the next diagram, the horizontal line indicates the path of some electrons in a cathode ray tube. Two wire grids are placed across the path at right angles to it. The grids are connected to a voltage source so that the electrons pass through the negative grid before reaching the positive grid. Under these conditions the voltage between the grids accelerates the electrons as they pass. Suppose an electron is moving slowly when it approaches the grids so that its kinetic energy is almost zero. If the grids boost the electron's speed to a magnitude v, then by equation (20) on page 58 they give it a kinetic energy equal to $\frac{1}{2}mv^2$. The source of this energy is the loss in potential energy experienced by the electron when it moves from the negative to the positive grid. The loss in potential energy per unit charge is called the *potential differ-ence*, usually expressed as the number of volts V. Since

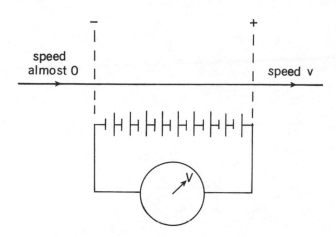

the charge on the electron is $-e$, its loss in potential energy is $-eV$. Since the potential energy lost is equal to the kinetic energy gained, we have

(40) $$\tfrac{1}{2}mv^2 = -eV.$$

Multiplying by 2 and dividing by e, we get

(41) $$\frac{m}{e}v^2 = -2V.$$

Step II. After the electrons acquire the speed v, a constant magnetic field of strength H is placed at right angles to the path of the electrons. Then the magnetic field exerts a force on each electron that compels it to move in a circle. By equation (16) on page 56, the force

77

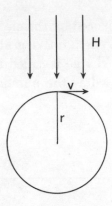

directed to the center of the circle is $e\dfrac{v}{c}H$. But this is the centripetal force, which, according to equation (35) is equal to mv^2/r, where r is the radius of the circle. Equating these two expressions, we get

(42)
$$e\,\frac{v}{c}\,H = \frac{mv^2}{r}.$$

Dividing by ev and multiplying by r, we get

(43)
$$\frac{m}{e}\,v = \frac{Hr}{c}.$$

Dividing equation (41) by equation (43) we get

(44)
$$v = \frac{-2cV}{Hr}.$$

Since c, the speed of light, is known, and V, H, and r can be measured in the experiment, equation (44) allows us to calculate the speed acquired by the electrons in Step I.

By equation (43), $m/e = (Hr/c) \div v$. Substituting for v the value given in equation (44), we get

$$\frac{m}{e} = \frac{Hr}{c} \div v$$

$$\frac{m}{e} = \frac{Hr}{c} \div \frac{-2cV}{Hr}$$

$$\frac{m}{e} = \frac{Hr}{c} \cdot \frac{Hr}{-2cV}$$

$$\frac{m}{e} = \frac{H^2r^2}{-2c^2V}.$$

Inverting both sides of the last equation, we get

(45) $$\frac{e}{m} = \frac{-2c^2V}{H^2r^2}.$$

Since c, V, H and r are all known, equation (45) allows us to calculate the ratio e/m.

Mass Varies with Speed

Repeated experiments like the one described above show that the ratio e/m is not constant but depends on the speed of the electron. This variability of e/m is accounted for by the theory of relativity which shows that the mass of a body depends on its speed with respect to the observer. If m_0 is the mass of an electron when it is at rest, and m is its mass when it moves with a speed v, then, according to the theory of relativity, m and m_0 are related as follows:

(46) $$m = \frac{m_0}{\sqrt{1 - \dfrac{v^2}{c^2}}}.$$

Substituting this value of m into equation (45), and then solving for e/m_0, we finally get

(47) $$\frac{e}{m_0} = \frac{-2c^2V}{H^2r^2 \sqrt{1 - \dfrac{v^2}{c^2}}},$$

from which the value of the ratio e/m_0 can be calculated. It is found that

(48) $$\frac{e}{m_0} = 5.3 \times 10^{17} \text{ esu per gram.}$$

Measuring e

In 1910, the magnitude of the electrostatic charge on an electron was measured in an ingenious experiment performed by Millikan. A tiny oil droplet was placed in the air space between the plates of a condenser, as shown in the diagram. The voltage between the plates was adjusted

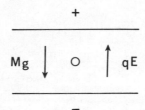

so that the upward push on the droplet exerted by the electrostatic field between the plates just balanced the downward pull of the weight of the droplet, so that the droplet remained stationary. If M is the mass of the droplet, and g is the acceleration due to gravity, then the downward pull, the weight of the droplet, according to equation (14), is given by Mg. If E is the force the electrostatic field would exert on a unit charge, and q is the charge on the droplet, the upward push on the droplet is qE. When the forces balance, $qE = Mg$, and therefore $q = Mg/E$. The quantity E, known as the *field strength* between the plates, can be measured. The mass M can be computed from the speed with which the oil droplet falls when the electric current is turned off. And g, the acceleration due to gravity, is known. Therefore q can be computed. Repeated measurements on many droplets showed that there is a smallest value e that q may have, and that all other values q may have are whole number multiples of e. Assuming that the smallest possible charge e is the magnitude of the charge of a single electron, the experiment gives us the value of e. It is found that

(49) $$e = 4.80 \times 10^{-10} \text{ esu.}$$

Computing m_0

Substituting this value of e into equation (48), we find the value of the mass of an electron at rest:

(50)
$$m_0 = (4.80 \times 10^{-10})(5.3 \times 10^{17}) \text{ gram}$$
$$= 9.11 \times 10^{-28} \text{ gram.}$$

Positive Charges in the Atom

In 1886 Goldstein used a cathode ray tube in which holes or canals had been drilled through the cathode. He found that while the negative cathode rays were flowing from the cathode (toward the anode), other positive rays were flowing through the canals of the cathode in the opposite direction. These are known as *canal rays*. In other experiments it was found, too, that positive rays sometimes flowed from the anode of a cathode ray tube. These are known as *anode rays*. The existence of these positive rays can be explained by assuming, as Thomson did, that there are positive charges as well as negatively charged electrons in every atom. Ordinarily, every positive charge of magnitude e in an atom is balanced by a negative

81

charge of $-e$ on an electron in the atom, and vice versa. Under these conditions, as we saw on page 55, the atom is electrically neutral. However, a neutral atom can acquire an electrostatic charge in several ways. For example, if one or more electrons are added to it, it acquires a negative charge. If one or more electrons are removed from it, it acquires a positive charge. An atom or cluster of atoms that has a charge is called an *ion*. The process of producing ions is called *ionization*. Using these concepts, the canal rays and the anode rays are explained in this way: As the electrons of the cathode rays stream through the tube they occasionally collide with molecules of the gas in the tube. Sometimes a collision is violent enough to tear an electron out of a molecule and ionize it. The resulting positive ion is attracted toward the negative cathode. Some of the ions hit the cathode and stick to it. Others pass through the canals in the cathode and form the canal rays. Electrons in the cathode rays also bombard the anode. Here they may tear electrons out of atoms in the anode. Positive ions torn out of the anode become the source of anode rays.

There are various ways of measuring the charge and the mass of an ion. The charge is always found to be an integral multiple of e. The mass is always found to agree with the known chemical composition of the ion. The ion with smallest mass and smallest positive charge is a hydrogen ion, with a charge of e.

Electrolytes

Additional evidence, produced by both chemists and physicists, supported the assumption that there are elec-

82

trical particles inside the atom. There are some chemical compounds, which, when dissolved in water, produce solutions capable of conducting an electric current. Such compounds are known as *electrolytes*. For example, hydrogen chloride is an electrolyte. If two electrodes connected to a source of direct current are inserted into a solution of hydrogen chloride, a current flows through the solution. Moreover, while the current flows, the hydrogen chloride is decomposed by it into hydrogen gas and chlorine gas. The hydrogen gas appears in bubbles on the cathode, and the chlorine gas appears in bubbles on the anode. The process of decomposing an electrolyte by means of an electric current is called *electrolysis*. In the electrolysis of copper bromide, metallic copper is deposited on the cathode, while bromine is deposited on the anode.

To explain the behavior of electrolytes, Arrhenius proposed in 1887 the theory that an electrolyte in solution dissociates into both positive and negative ions. The positive ions are attracted toward the cathode where they pick up enough electrons to become neutral atoms or molecules. The negative ions are attracted toward the anode where they give up enough electrons to become neutral atoms or molecules. The charge on an ion is accounted for by a shortage of electrons in a positive ion, and an excess of electrons in a negative ion. The number of electrons short or in excess in an atomic ion is the valence of the ion. A hydrogen atom that is short one electron is denoted by H^+ and has a valence of 1. A chlorine atom that has one electron too many is denoted by Cl^- and also has a valence of 1. A copper atom that has a shortage of two electrons is denoted by Cu^{++}, and has a valence of 2.

Gram-atom

In experiments with electrolysis Faraday discovered a relationship between the quantity of charge transported through an electrolytic solution and the quantity of an element deposited on an electrode. Before stating what this relationship is, it is necessary to introduce the concept of a *gram-atom* of an element. It is related to the concept of standard volume described on page 34. The standard volume of 22.4 liters of a compound in the gaseous state has the property that, at standard temperature and pressure, the number of grams of the compound that it contains is equal to the number of amu in the molecular weight of the compound. This same number of grams of the compound, whether it is in the gaseous, liquid or solid state, is called a *gram-molecule* of the compound. Analogously, that weight of an element that contains as many grams of the element as there are amu in the atomic weight of the element is called a *gram-atom*. For example, since the atomic weight of hydrogen is 1.008 amu, a gram-atom of hydrogen is 1.008 grams of hydrogen. Since the atomic weight of chlorine is 35.457 amu, a gram-atom of chlorine is 35.457 grams of chlorine.

We have already seen that a standard volume of 22.4 liters of a gas at standard temperature and pressure always contains the same number of molecules, namely, N_o molecules, where N_o is Avogadro's number. It follows, then, that a gram-molecule of a compound contains N_o molecules of the compound. We now show that, similarly, a gram-atom of an element contains N_o atoms.

Let the atomic weight of an element be w amu. Then

the weight of a gram-atom of the element is w grams. Let N be the number of atoms in a gram-atom of the element. Since each atom weighs w amu, then N atoms weigh Nw amu. Consequently, w grams $= Nw$ amu $= Nw$ (1 amu). We saw on page 38 that 1 amu $= 1/N_o$ gram. Substituting this value for 1 amu, we find that

$$w \text{ grams} = Nw \left(\frac{1}{N_o} \text{ gram} \right).$$

Multiplying by N_o and dividing by w, we find that N grams $= N_o$ grams, that is, that $N = N_o$. *The number of atoms in a gram-atom of an element is Avogadro's number.*

Faraday's Law

Faraday discovered in 1833 that when a fixed amount of charge is passed through an electrolytic solution, the mass of an element deposited on an electrode is proportional to the equivalent weight, which is the atomic weight divided by the valence. In particular there is a certain definite amount of charge needed to deposit a weight of an element equal to a gram-atom divided by the valence. This definite amount is known as Faraday's constant. It is denoted by F and has the value 2.90×10^{14} esu.

The fact observed by Faraday is easily explained on the basis of the ionic theory of electrolytes. Suppose an element deposited on the cathode during electrolysis has atomic weight w. Then a gram-atom of the element contains w grams of the element, and, as we have seen, consists of N_o atoms. Suppose a positive ion of the element

85

lacks n electrons. Then the valence of the element in this ion is n. Since w grams of the element contains N_o atoms, $\frac{w}{n}$ grams of the element contain N_o/n atoms. To convert one ion into a neutral atom deposited on the cathode, n electrons are needed (one for each electron it lacks). To convert N_o/n ions into the same number of atoms, $(N_o/n) \times n$ electrons are needed. So, N_o electrons are needed to deposit a weight of w/n grams of an element whose valence is n. Then the charge F measured by Faraday is the magnitude of the charge of N_o electrons, that is,

$$(51) \qquad F = eN_o,$$

where e is the magnitude of the charge of one electron. F is a constant because e and N_o are constants.

Avogadro's Number

If we divide both sides of equation (51) by e, we get

$$(52) \qquad N_o = \frac{F}{e},$$

from which Avogadro's number can be computed. Since $F = 2.9 \times 10^{14}$ esu, and $e = 4.8 \times 10^{-10}$ esu,

$$(53) \qquad N_o = \frac{2.9 \times 10^{14}}{4.8 \times 10^{-10}} = 6 \times 10^{23}, \text{ approximately.}$$

Radioactivity

More evidence that there are electrical particles in the atom was provided by the phenomenon of *radioactivity*. Atoms of uranium, radium and thorium spontaneously

86

release rays. Three distinct kinds of rays were identified, and given the names *alpha rays, beta rays,* and *gamma rays.* The alpha rays were found to be streams of particles each of which is a helium ion, with a charge of $2e$. These particles are called alpha particles. The beta rays were found to be streams of particles each of which is an electron. The gamma rays were found to be electromagnetic radiation of very high frequency. When an atom of a radioactive element releases either an alpha particle or a beta particle the atom is transformed into an atom of a *different element.*

A Building Block for Atoms

The atomic weights of some elements are very nearly whole numbers of amu. This is shown, for example, in the partial list of elements printed below:

Element	Atomic weight (number of amu)
Hydrogen	1.008
Helium	4.003
Beryllium	9.013
Carbon	12.010
Nitrogen	14.008
Oxygen	16.000
Fluorine	19.00

This fact suggested to Prout in 1815 the idea that the smallest atom, hydrogen, with atomic weight of about 1 amu, might be the building block out of which all other atoms are made. According to Prout's hypothesis, a helium atom has an atomic weight of about 4 amu because it contains 4 hydrogen atoms; a carbon atom has an atomic weight of about 12 amu because it contains 12 hydrogen atoms; etc. Prout's hypothesis was not widely supported at first because there are many elements whose atomic weights are not close to a whole number of amu. For example, the atomic weight of chlorine is 35.457. However, a later discovery gave strong support to Prout's hypothesis, and in a modified form it has become part of the modern theory of the atom.

Chemical Twins

Prout's hypothesis was revived when it was discovered by Thomson, Aston and others that the atoms of some elements are not all identical. Chlorine, for example, is a mixture of two different kinds of atoms that are the same in their chemical behavior but have different atomic weights. Moreover the atomic weights of these different kinds of chlorine atoms are almost whole numbers of amu, namely 35 amu and 37 amu. Atoms that are chemically the same but have different weights are called *isotopes*. By now, every element has been found to have two or more isotopes, and the atomic weight of every isotope of an element has been found to be nearly a whole number of amu. It is clear then that the whole number nearest to the atomic weight of an isotope of an element must have some physical meaning. The whole number nearest to the atomic weight of an isotope is called its *mass number*, and is designated by the symbol A.

Since every element is a mixture of isotopes, the atomic weight of an element depends on how much of each isotope is in the mixture. For example, 75% of all chlorine atoms have an atomic weight of 35 amu, and the remaining 25% have an atomic weight of 37 amu. Consequently the mixture has an atomic weight of (.75 × 35 amu) + (.25 × 37 amu) = 35.5 amu, approximately. All fractional atomic weights can be explained in the same way.

The Nucleus of the Atom

In 1911 Rutherford tried to get information about the structure of atoms by throwing small fast-moving parti-

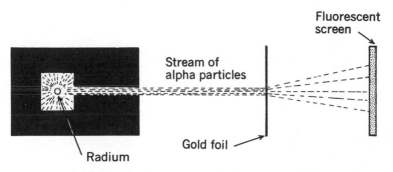

Schematic diagram of the experiment in which Rutherford discovered the nucleus

cles at them. The atoms he bombarded were atoms of gold in a thin sheet of gold foil. The particles he threw at them were alpha particles released by the radioactive disintegration of radium. Some of the alpha particles passed right through the gold foil as if there were nothing there. Others were deflected as if they had passed close to a positive charge. The detailed results of the experiment could be explained by the assumption that each atom consists of a central core or *nucleus* with a positive charge, surrounded by enough electrons to make the total charge on the atom equal to zero.

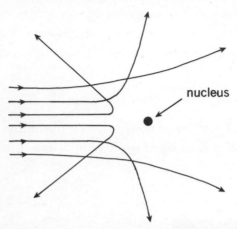

Deflection of alpha particles by positive charge of nucleus

From the paths followed by the deflected alpha particles Rutherford calculated the deflecting force exerted by the nucleus on an alpha particle at a distance r. The force turned out to be $2Ze^2/r^2$, where Z is the atomic number of the atom, and e is the amount of charge given by equation (49). By equation (15) on page 56, this is precisely the force exerted by a charge Q on another charge q, if $Q = Ze$, and $q = 2e$. Since an alpha particle has charge $2e$, Rutherford concluded that the charge Ze must be the charge on the nucleus. To balance this charge, there must be Z electrons surrounding the nucleus. Later experiments by Moseley, in which he examined the X rays produced when different elements were bombarded by cathode rays, confirmed Rutherford's discovery that the atomic number Z of an atom is a measure of the charge on its nucleus, using e as the unit of charge. This discovery casts new light on the order of the elements in the periodic table of the elements. The place of an element in the table depends on the charge on the nucleus of an atom of the element, rather than its atomic weight.

Particles in the Nucleus

Nearly all the mass of an atom is in the nucleus of the atom. Since the mass of an isotope of an atom is nearly a whole number of amu, the mass of its nucleus is nearly a whole number of amu. This fact leads to a modification of Prout's hypothesis. Prout assumed that an atom whose mass number is A contains A hydrogen atoms, each with a mass of 1 amu. The modified version of Prout's hypothesis asserts instead that the *nucleus* of an atom with mass number A contains A hydrogen *nuclei*, each with a mass of 1 amu.

The hydrogen nucleus with mass 1 amu is called a *proton*. The charge on a proton is e. Consequently A protons have a total charge of Ae. However, the charge on a nucleus is Ze, and for all atoms except the hydrogen atom with mass number 1 the atomic number Z is less than the mass number A. For example, in the most common isotope of helium, while the mass number is 4, the atomic number is only 2. This fact makes it necessary to modify Prout's hypothesis even further.

The Proton-Electron Theory of the Nucleus

The discrepancy between the mass number A and the atomic number Z of an atom could be accounted for if the nucleus contained not only protons, but also electrons that balanced the charge of some of the protons. For example, if we assume that a helium nucleus contains 4 protons and 2 electrons, its charge would be $4e - 2e = 2e$, so its atomic number would be 2. Moreover, since the 2 electrons contribute a negligible amount of mass to the nucleus, its mass would be about 4 amu (the mass of the 4 protons), and hence its mass number would be 4. In general, if an atom has mass number A and atomic number Z, we could account for the discrepancy between A and Z by assuming that the nucleus contains A protons and enough electrons to neutralize the charge of all but Z of the protons. These considerations led to the theory that a nucleus with mass number A and atomic number Z consists of A protons and $A - Z$ electrons.

The theory broke down, however, when it was discovered that the nuclei of atoms are spinning like tops and hence have angular momentum. The proton-electron theory of the nucleus turned out to be inconsistent with measurements made of nuclear angular momentum.*

Discovery of the Neutron

A different and better version of Prout's hypothesis became possible with the discovery of the *neutron*. Experiments in which alpha particles were thrown at atoms of beryllium or boron caused the bombarded atoms to eject electrically neutral particles. It was thought at first that these were gamma rays. However, in 1932, Chadwick showed that they were particles that had the same mass

* For details, see *Inside the Nucleus,* by the same author, The John Day Company, New York, 1963.

as protons, namely about 1 amu each. Because they are electrically neutral, these particles are known as neutrons.

The new and final version of Prout's hypothesis takes this form: If a nucleus has mass number A and atomic number Z, the nucleus consists of Z protons and $A - Z$ neutrons. The Z protons account for the atomic number Z. The total number of particles of mass 1 amu is A, and this accounts for the mass number A. It is found, too, that this theory fits the known facts about nuclear angular momentum.

A Model of the Atom

The facts and theories outlined in the preceding pages culminated in the construction of the following theoretical model of an atom:

Every atom consists of a nucleus surrounded by planetary electrons. If the mass number of the atom is A and its atomic number is Z, the nucleus contains A particles of mass about 1 amu each. Z of them are protons, and the remaining $A - Z$ of them are neutrons. The charge on the nucleus is Ze, the charge of the Z protons. The number of electrons that surround the nucleus is the same as the number of protons that are in the nucleus.

This is only a crude model, because while it tells us how many electrons surround a nucleus in an atom, it does not tell us how these electrons are arranged. In the chapters that follow we show how the model has been refined in order to give precise information about the arrangement of the electrons around the nucleus.

V

Atoms of Light

THE next steps in the development of the theory of atomic structure were based on studying the interaction of atoms and electromagnetic radiation. The form that the theory was compelled to take was determined in large part by the discovery that electromagnetic radiation, like matter, is not continuous, but is made up of discrete units. In this chapter we outline the experimental data and the theoretical ideas that converged toward this discovery.

Black Body Radiation

In the theory of heat, a body that absorbs all the electromagnetic radiant energy that falls on it is called a *black body*. Every body whose temperature is above zero degrees Kelvin radiates energy into space. In the case of a black body, the amount of radiation and its distribution among different frequencies depend only on the temperature of the body. A box that is closed except for one small opening into the cavity it encloses behaves like a black body: Radiation that falls on the opening from the outside enters the cavity and is reflected back and forth between the walls of the box until it is completely absorbed. Consequently any radiation that emerges from the opening has the characteristics of black body radiation. With the help of thermodynamic theory and the electromagnetic theory of light, two laws governing black body radiation can be derived. One, known as *Stefan's law,* asserts that if the Kelvin temperature of the body is T, the total amount of energy the body radiates is proportional to T^4. The other law, known as *Wien's law,* asserts that the formula for u_f, the rate per unit of frequency at which this total is shared among different frequencies, takes the form

(54) $$u_f = f^3 \times F\left(\frac{f}{T}\right),$$

where the symbol $F\left(\frac{f}{T}\right)$ stands for a function of $\frac{f}{T}$, that is, a variable whose value depends on the value of the ratio $\frac{f}{T}$. Thermodynamic theory does not specify what this function is.

Planck's Quantum Hypothesis

In 1900 Planck undertook to identify the function F that occurs in Wien's law. To do so, he had to make some assumptions about the mechanism that produces the radiation from a black body. According to thermodynamic theory, the function F should be the same no matter what the mechanism is, so he naturally used the simplest assumptions that he could. He assumed that the oscillator that produces radiation with frequency f is an electric charge vibrating with frequency f. On the basis of

96

this assumption he could show that u_f is related to E, the average energy of the oscillator, by the formula

$$(55) \qquad u_f = \frac{8\pi f^2}{c^3} E.$$

If, in addition, he assumed that the energy radiated by the oscillator is divisible into arbitrarily small amounts, he could show that E is related to the temperature T by the formula,

$$(56) \qquad E = kT,$$

where k is a constant known as Boltzmann's constant. Substituting this value of E into equation (55) gives

$$(57) \qquad u_f = \frac{8\pi f^2}{c^3} kT.$$

Multiplying the right hand side of this equation by $\dfrac{f}{f}$ (which is equal to 1), we find that it can also be written in the form

$$(58) \qquad u_f = \frac{8\pi f^3}{c^3} k \frac{T}{f} = f^3 \times \frac{8\pi k}{c^3 \left(\dfrac{f}{T}\right)}.$$

Comparing equation (58) with equation (54), we see that this result agrees with Wien's law, because $8\pi k / \left[c^3 \left(\dfrac{f}{T} \right) \right]$ is a function of $\dfrac{f}{T}$. However, it *does not agree with experimental fact*. Equation (57) implies that the higher the frequency f is, the higher the value of u_f is. The fact is, however, that as we examine higher and higher frequencies, u_f at first increases to a maximum, and then *decreases* again.

97

Since the assumptions he used led to a formula that is wrong, Planck re-examined his assumptions to see what changes he should make in order to derive a formula that is right. One of the assumptions was that the energy radiated by the oscillator is divisible into arbitrarily small amounts. He replaced this assumption by the opposite assumption that the energy is radiated only in whole number multiples of an indivisible small amount called a *quantum*. Under this assumption, if the quantum of energy is represented by the symbol ϵ (epsilon), he showed that equation (56) is replaced by

$$(59) \qquad E = \frac{\epsilon}{e^{\frac{\epsilon}{kT}} - 1},$$

where e is approximately 2.718. Substituting this value of E into equation (55) gives

$$(60) \qquad u_f = \frac{8\pi f^2}{c^3} \times \frac{\epsilon}{e^{\frac{\epsilon}{kT}} - 1}.$$

According to Wien's law, the temperature T should enter into the formula only in the ratio $\frac{f}{T}$. So, to make equation (60) have the form prescribed by equation (54), Planck made the assumption that

$$(61) \qquad \epsilon = hf,$$

where h is a constant. Substituting this value of ϵ into equation (60) yields the formula

$$(62) \qquad u_f = \frac{8\pi h f^3}{c^3} \times \frac{1}{e^{\frac{h}{k}\left(\frac{f}{T}\right)} - 1},$$

in which u_f is seen to be the product of f^3 and a function of f/T, as prescribed by Wien's law. Equation (62) is known as *Planck's law*. It is fully confirmed by the facts of experiment. The constant h is known as *Planck's constant*, and has been found to have the value 6.62×10^{-27} erg second.

The Photon

Planck merely assumed that the quantum of energy hf was the smallest amount of electromagnetic energy with frequency f that can be *radiated*. In 1905, Einstein carried the quantum idea one step further by assuming that the quantum hf was the smallest amount of electromagnetic energy of frequency f that can *exist*, and that in fact a beam of light of frequency f is a stream of indivisible corpuscles each of which contains an amount of energy equal to hf. These corpuscles are called *photons*. By making this assumption he was able to explain the hitherto unexplained details of the *photoelectric effect*. If ultraviolet light is allowed to fall on a metal surface kept in a vacuum tube, the light knocks electrons out of the surface. If a voltage is applied to the tube, the electrons move to produce an electric current. It is then possible to measure the current, which is proportional to the number of electrons knocked out. It is also possible to measure the speed of the electrons when they are ejected from the metal surface. It turns out that increasing the intensity of the light increases the number of electrons knocked out, but does not increase the speed of the electrons. In fact the kinetic energy of each electron knocked out depends only on the frequency of the light, and is given by the formula $hf - A$, where A is a constant whose value depends on the metal that was irradiated.

If we assume as Einstein did that a beam of light of frequency f is a stream of photons each with energy hf, then these facts are easily explained. An electron is knocked out of the surface by the light when a photon of light collides with the electron. In this collision, the photon delivers all of its energy, an amount equal to hf, to the electron. Part of this energy, an amount equal to A, is used up to overcome the force holding the electron in place in the metal. The balance, $hf - A$, gives the electron its kinetic energy. When the intensity of the beam of light is increased, more photons strike the metal, and more electrons are knocked out.

The theory that light is made up of photons is confirmed in an experiment with X rays performed by Compton in 1922. X rays passed through a block of paraffin are scattered by the electrons in the paraffin. According to the wave theory of light, if radiation with frequency f is scattered in any direction, the scattered radiation should also have frequency f. However, Compton's experiment showed that if the radiation is turned aside through an angle that is less than 90°, the scattered radiation has a frequency that is lower than f. This result is easily explained by the photon theory. When a photon with energy hf collides with an electron, it passes some of its energy on to the electron. Therefore the photon that leaves the scene of the collision has an amount of energy hf' that is less than hf. But if $hf' < hf$, then dividing by h, we find that $f' < f$. That is, the frequency f' of the scattered photon is less than the frequency f of the original photon.

The Momentum of a Photon

Since a photon striking an electron is capable of making it move, a photon has momentum. To compute the momentum of a photon, we make use of the fact predicted by relativity theory and confirmed by experiment, that mass and energy are equivalent. The equivalence is expressed in the equation

$$(63) \qquad E = mc^2,$$

where E is the energy equivalent to a mass m, and vice versa. Dividing both sides of equation (63) by c^2 we get

$$(64) \qquad m = \frac{E}{c^2}.$$

According to equation (11) on page 52, the momentum M of a particle with mass m and speed v is given by $M = mv$. If a photon has energy E, the mass that E is equivalent to is given by equation (64), and the speed at which it moves is c. Substituting these values into equation (11), we get

$$(65) \qquad M = \frac{E}{c^2} \times c = \frac{E}{c}.$$

However, by equation (61), $E = hf$, and by equation (38) on page 71, $f\lambda = c$. Substituting these values of E and c into equation (65), we get this formula for the momentum of a photon:

$$(66) \qquad M = \frac{hf}{f\lambda} = \frac{h}{\lambda}.$$

VI

The Hydrogen Atom

The Atom as a Radiator

UNDER certain special conditions, an atom becomes "excited" and *radiates* light. For example, when some table salt is sprinkled into a gas flame, some of the salt is vaporized. Then sodium atoms in the vapor are excited by the heat of the flame and glow with a bright yellow light. Another example is seen in the neon signs used in advertising displays, where an electric current is passed through a tube containing neon gas at low pressure. The atoms of neon, excited by the current, glow with a red light. In general, if atoms in a low pressure gas are made very hot, or are bombarded by electrons, they become excited and radiate light.

The light radiated by excited atoms in a vapor of an element is a mixture of light with different wavelengths. If a narrow beam of the light is passed through a diffraction grating, the different wavelengths are separated in the spectrum that is formed. Each wavelength shows up as a bright line in the spectrum. The wavelength λ of each line can be calculated by the method described on page 69. Its frequency f can be calculated by using equation (38) on page 71, and its wave number ν can be

103

calculated by using equation (39), on page 72. Every element has a characteristic spectrum containing certain particular lines and no others. This set of lines is called the *emission spectrum* of the element.

An atom can also *absorb* light. White light is a mixture of the colors in the rainbow. If white light is passed through a low pressure gas of an element the atoms in the gas absorb some of the colors. The spectrum of white light before it passes through the gas is a continuous band of the colors of the rainbow, arranged according to wavelength, from red to violet. In the spectrum of white light that has passed through the gas, dark lines appear in the bright rainbow band of colors. Each dark line indicates the wavelength of some light that has been absorbed by atoms of the gas. The set of dark lines is called the *absorption spectrum* of the element.

The emission spectrum and the absorption spectrum of an element contain clues about the structure of an atom of the element. In this chapter we examine these clues and show how Niels Bohr used them to build the first important model of atomic structure.

The Hydrogen Spectrum

In the investigation of atomic structure, it was natural to start by studying the simplest of all atoms, the hydrogen atom, which consists of a nucleus and one planetary electron. The study begins with an examination of the hydrogen spectrum. The emission spectrum of hydrogen includes a discrete series of lines of visible light of different wavelengths, as shown in the next diagram. This series is known as the *Balmer* series. The first line on the

104

left in the series is designated as H_α, and is made by light whose wavelength is .00006563 centimeter. The second line, H_β, is made by light whose wavelength is .00004861 centimeter. The third line, H_γ, is made by light whose wavelength is .00004340 centimeter. The successive lines

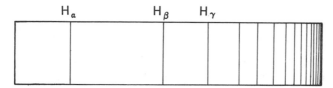

H$_\alpha$ H$_\beta$ H$_\gamma$

The Balmer series in the hydrogen spectrum

in the series are closer and closer together, and converge toward a line representing light whose wavelength is .00003646 centimeter. Beyond this line, the spectrum is a continuous band.

In 1885, Balmer showed that the wave numbers corresponding to the lines in the series can be computed from the formula

$$(67) \qquad \nu = R\left(\frac{1}{4} - \frac{1}{m^2}\right),$$

where m is any whole number greater than 2, and R is a constant. R is known as the *Rydberg constant* and has the value 109678 per centimeter. The line H_α is obtained when $m = 3$, H_β is obtained when $m = 4$, H_γ is obtained when $m = 5$, and so on. For example, using $m = 3$, we get

$$\nu = 109678\left(\frac{1}{4} - \frac{1}{9}\right) = 109678\left(\frac{5}{36}\right)$$
$$= \frac{548390}{36}.$$

By equation (39), $\nu = \frac{1}{\lambda}$. Consequently $\lambda = \frac{1}{\nu} =$ 36/548390. If this division is carried out, the quotient is found to agree with the measured value $\lambda = .00006563$ centimeter given above for H_α.

Invisible Lines

Since $4 = 2^2$, Balmer's formula can also be written in this form:

$$\nu = R\left(\frac{1}{2^2} - \frac{1}{m^2}\right).$$

This suggests a generalization of the formula:

$$(68) \qquad \nu = R\left(\frac{1}{n^2} - \frac{1}{m^2}\right),$$

where n is any positive integer, and m is any integer greater than n. The Balmer series is obtained when we choose $n = 2$. Are there, perhaps, other series of lines in the hydrogen spectrum that correspond to other choices of the value of n? It has been found that there are. The Balmer series was discovered first because it is in the visible part of the electromagnetic spectrum and can be seen with the eye. The other lines consist of lines of ultraviolet light or infrared light, which are invisible, but can be detected by special instruments. The series corresponding to values of n from 1 to 5 are listed below, together with the name of the man who discovered it, the date of discovery, and the region of the spectrum in which the series is found:

$n = 1$, Lyman, 1916, ultraviolet
$n = 2$, Balmer, 1885, visible

$n = 3$, Paschen, 1908, infrared
$n = 4$, Brackett, 1922, infrared
$n = 5$, Pfund, 1924, infrared

A Model that Failed

A basic requirement for a model of the hydrogen atom is that it fit the known facts about the behavior of the atom as a radiator of electromagnetic energy. The basic facts are: 1) the atom normally does not radiate energy. It radiates energy only when it is in an excited state. 2) It can radiate light of only certain fixed frequencies, some of which form discrete series such as the Balmer series.

The first model that was constructed pictured the hydrogen atom as a sort of miniature solar system in which an electron revolves around the nucleus just as the earth revolves around the sun, and obeying the ordinary laws of electricity. According to these laws, the electron could be at any arbitrary distance from the nucleus. As it revolved around the nucleus, the electron would radiate electromagnetic energy all the time and the frequency of the radiation would be equal to the frequency of its revolutions around the nucleus. Moreover, as the electron loses energy by radiating some of it, its frequency of revolution, and hence the frequency of the light radiated would change continuously, so that the emission spectrum of hydrogen would be continuous, instead of having any discrete series of lines in it. These predictions are contradicted by the facts, because the atom does not radiate all the time, and its emission spectrum is not continuous.

Energy Levels in the Atom

Because of the failure of the "solar system" model of the atom, a new one had to be constructed. Niels Bohr constructed the first substantially successful model in 1913. Before presenting the assumptions he made, we develop the sequence of ideas that led him to them.

Equation (68) gives a formula for the wave number ν of each line in the hydrogen spectrum. By equation (39) of page 72, $f = c\nu$, so if we multiply both sides of equation (68) by c, we get a formula for the frequency of each line in the spectrum:

$$(69) \qquad f = c\nu = cR \left(\frac{1}{n^2} - \frac{1}{m^2} \right).$$

The light in a line of the spectrum that corresponds to given values of m and n consists of photons having the frequency given by equation (69). According to the quantum theory of Planck and Einstein, the energy of a photon is given by $\epsilon = hf$. So, if we multiply both sides of equation (69) by h, we get a formula for the energy of a photon radiated by a hydrogen atom:

$$(70) \qquad \epsilon = hf = chR \left(\frac{1}{n^2} - \frac{1}{m^2} \right).$$

Consequently,

$$(71) \qquad \epsilon = \frac{chR}{n^2} - \frac{chR}{m^2}.$$

Notice that the energy of the photon is the difference between two terms of the same form. This fact suggested to Bohr the idea that each of these terms represents an

108

amount of energy that may be possessed by the electron in the hydrogen atom. If one term gives the energy the electron has before it radiates the photon, and the other term gives the energy it has after it radiates the photon, then the energy radiated in the photon is the difference between these two terms. Consequently Bohr made these assumptions:

1. The possible values of the energy that may be possessed by the electron in the hydrogen atom are given by the formula

$$(72) \qquad E_n = -\frac{chR}{n^2},$$

where n may be any positive integer. The integer n is called a *quantum number*. The values E_1, E_2, E_3, etc., given by this formula, are called the *energy levels* of the electron in the atom. We may represent these levels schematically by a series of horizontal lines, as shown in the diagram on page 111.

2. As long as the electron remains on a fixed energy level, it does not radiate any energy. In particular, it does not radiate any energy if it is on the level E_1. This level is known as the *ground state*.

3. If, by a collision, or some other means, an amount of energy equal to $E_n - E_1$, with $n > 1$, is added to the electron in the ground state, the electron is "pushed up" to the level E_n. Each level E_n, with $n > 1$, is known as an *excited state*.

4. An electron in an excited state E_n spontaneously "falls" to a "lower" energy level. The energy ϵ it loses when it falls from one level to another is radiated as a

109

photon, and the frequency of the photon is determined by the equation $\epsilon = hf$.

By assumption 4, when the electron falls from the m'th energy level to the n'th energy level, where $m > n$, it radiates a photon whose energy ϵ is given by

$$(73) \qquad \epsilon = E_m - E_n.$$

If we substitute hf for ϵ, and substitute for E_m and E_n the values given by equation (72), we get equation (70). If we divide equation (70) by h, we get equation (69). Then, if we divide equation (69) by c, we get equation (68). Thus, Bohr's assumptions successfully account for the particular lines that appear in the spectrum of hydrogen. If an electron falls to E_1 from a higher level, it radiates a photon that helps produce one of the lines in the Lyman series. If it falls to E_2 from a higher level, it radiates a photon that helps produce one of the lines in the Balmer series, etc. In an excited gas, there are many excited atoms, not all on the same energy level. While each radiating atom radiates only one frequency at a time, determined by equation (73), many atoms radiate many frequencies simultaneously, and thus produce the many lines of the spectrum.

The Bohr Model of the Atom

Bohr's concept of energy levels in the atom is the heart of his model of the atom. However, he carried the model one step further by picturing each energy level as an orbit along which the electron in the atom may move. To obtain this picture, he made the following assumptions to take the place of assumption 1:

110

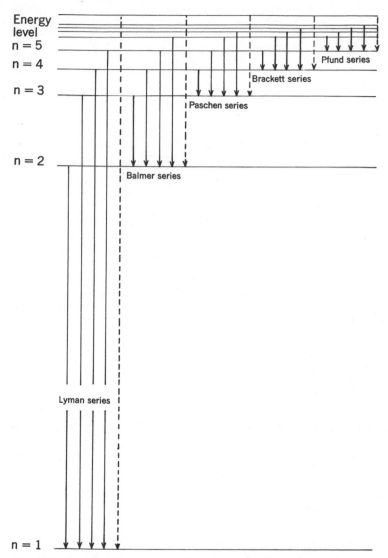

Energy levels in the hydrogen atom, and electron falls that produce the Lyman series, Balmer series, Paschen series, Brackett series and Pfund series

111

1A. The electron in the hydrogen atom moves in circular orbits around the nucleus. There is an orbit that corresponds to each possible energy level.

1B. The possible orbits are those and only those in which the angular momentum p has a value $nh/2\pi$, where n is any positive integer, and h is Planck's constant.

Using assumptions 1A and 1B, it is possible to derive equation (72) as a consequence. It is also possible to derive a formula for R, the Rydberg constant, and a formula for the radius r of each possible circular orbit. Since the derivation of these results involves only elementary mathematics applied to ideas already introduced, we shall carry out the derivations in full. In order to simplify the computations, we temporarily make one additional assumption, that the nucleus of the atom is stationary, and only the electron revolving around it moves. We shall discard this assumption later.

Hydrogen-like Atoms

In the hydrogen atom we are dealing with a nucleus whose charge is $1e$, and an electron whose charge is $-e$. However, we shall assume more generally that the nucleus has a charge Ze. Then our results will be applicable not only to the hydrogen atom $(Z = 1)$, but also to other hydrogen-like atoms, where $Z \neq 1$. For example, the helium ion He^+ has a nucleus whose charge is $2e$, so $Z = 2$. But it is hydrogen-like in that it has only one planetary electron. Other atoms may also be thought of as hydrogen-like in this sense. Consider the behavior of only one electron at a time. This electron is attracted by

112

the charge on the nucleus, and repelled by the charge on each other electron in the atom. However, the influence of the nucleus predominates, because the magnitude of its charge is much greater than that of any one electron. In fact, the average effect of the other electrons is approximately like that of a shield, reducing the effective charge of the nucleus. Let Ze be the reduced effective charge on the nucleus. Then the electron whose motion is being studied behaves like the electron in a hydrogen-like atom whose nucleus has charge Ze.

Equations of the Bohr Theory

We assume then, that the nucleus has charge Ze, and that the electron, whose charge is $-e$, is in a circular orbit around the nucleus. Let $r =$ the radius of the orbit, $m =$ the rest mass of the electron, $v =$ the speed of the electron, and $E =$ the total energy of the electron. The total energy of the electron is made up of two parts, its potential energy in the electrostatic field surrounding the nucleus, and its kinetic energy. The potential energy is given by equation (33) on page 64, with $Q = Ze$, and $q = -e$. Making these substitutions, we find that

$$\text{the potential energy} = -\frac{Ze^2}{r}.$$

The kinetic energy is given by equation (20). Adding these two amounts, we get

(74) $$E = -\frac{Ze^2}{r} + \frac{1}{2}mv^2.$$

By equation (35) on page 68, the magnitude of the centripetal force acting on the electrons as it moves around

113

the circle is mv^2/r. However, this force is actually the electrostatic force of attraction between the nucleus and the electron. By equation (15) on page 56, the electrostatic force is Qq/r^2, where, in this case, $Q = Ze$, and $q = -e$. Making these substitutions, we find that the force is $-Ze^2/r^2$, where the minus sign indicates that it is a force of attraction. The magnitude of the force (its size without regard to its direction) is therefore Ze^2/r^2. Equating this expression to the magnitude of the centripetal force, we get

$$(75) \qquad \frac{Ze^2}{r^2} = \frac{mv^2}{r}.$$

Multiplying both sides of this equation by r, we get

$$(76) \qquad \frac{Ze^2}{r} = mv^2.$$

Consequently, we may substitute mv^2 for Ze^2/r. Making this substitution in equation (74), we get

$$(77) \qquad E = -mv^2 + \tfrac{1}{2}mv^2 = -\tfrac{1}{2}mv^2.$$

If we multiply equation (77) by -2, we get

$$(78) \qquad mv^2 = -2E.$$

If we replace mv^2 in equation (77) by Ze^2/r, we get

$$(79) \qquad E = -\tfrac{1}{2}\left(\frac{Ze^2}{r}\right).$$

Solving equation (79) for r, we get

$$(80) \qquad r = -\frac{Ze^2}{2E}.$$

Bohr's assumption 1B says that the angular momentum p of the orbital motion of the electron is $nh/2\pi$. By equa-

114

tion (37) on page 68, the angular momentum p is equal to mvr. Equating these two expressions for p, we get

$$(81) \qquad rmv = \frac{nh}{2\pi}.$$

Squaring both sides of equation (81), we get

$$(82) \qquad r^2 m^2 v^2 = \frac{n^2 h^2}{4\pi^2}, \quad \text{or}$$

$$(r^2 m)(mv^2) = \frac{n^2 h^2}{4\pi^2}.$$

Substituting into the last equation the value of r given by equation (80), and the value of mv^2 given by equation (78), we get

$$(83) \qquad \left(-\frac{Ze^2}{2e} \right) 2m \; (-2E) = \frac{n^2 h^2}{4\pi^2}.$$

Solving equation (83) for E, we get

$$(84) \qquad E = -\frac{2\pi^2 m Z^2 e^4}{n^2 h^2}.$$

This equation is the equivalent of equation (72), since, as in equation (72), n^2 appears in the denominator of the expression for energy, and all the other quantities in the expression are constants. In fact, if we equate the two expressions for energy given by equations (72) and (84) we are able to derive a formula for the Rydberg constant:

$$(85) \qquad -\frac{chR}{n^2} = -\frac{2\pi^2 m Z^2 e^4}{n^2 h^2}.$$

Solving equation (85) for R, we get

$$(86) \qquad R = \frac{2\pi^2 m Z^2 e^4}{ch^3}.$$

115

This computation has been based on the temporary assumption that the nucleus is stationary. This assumption is false, however. Actually, both the nucleus and the electron revolve around their common center of mass. If the motion of the nucleus is taken into account, it turns out, for reasons that we need not go into, that the correct value of R is obtained by multiplying the value given in equation (86) by the factor $Z^2/\left(1 + \dfrac{m}{M}\right)$, where m is the mass of the electron and M is the mass of the nucleus. Thus we get the corrected formula

$$(87) \qquad R = \frac{2\pi^2 m Z^2 e^4}{ch^3}\left(\frac{Z^2}{1 + \dfrac{m}{M}}\right).$$

In the case of the hydrogen atom, $Z = 1$. So the formula for the Rydberg constant is

$$(88) \qquad R = \frac{2\pi^2 m e^4}{ch^3\left(1 + \dfrac{m}{M}\right)}.$$

If we substitute the value $m = 9.11 \times 10^{-28}$ gram (see page 81), the value $e = 4.80 \times 10^{-10}$ esu (see page 81), the value $c = 3 \times 10^{10}$ centimeters per second (see page 71), the value $h = 6.62 \times 10^{-27}$ erg second (see page 99), and the value $M =$ the mass of the hydrogen nucleus $= 1$ amu $= 1.66 \times 10^{-24}$ gram (see page 38), we can compute the value of R from the formula. The computed value obtained in this way from the Bohr theory agrees with the measured value given on page 105.

Equation (80) expresses the radius of each orbit in terms of the energy E that the electron has in that orbit. By substituting for E the value given by equation (84), we get a formula for r in terms of the quantum number n:

$$(89) \qquad r = \frac{n^2 h^2}{4\pi^2 m Z e^2}.$$

There is a different value for r for each value of n. In the hydrogen atom, $Z = 1$. For the ground state of the electron, the quantum number n has the value 1. Substituting $Z = 1$ and $n = 1$, we obtain a formula for the radius of the orbit of the electron when it is in the ground state:

$$(90) \qquad r = \frac{h^2}{4\pi^2 m e^2}.$$

This is the radius usually referred to as the radius of the hydrogen atom. Substituting the values of h, m and e given above, we find by computation that

(91)   the radius of the hydrogen atom = .529 $\times$ 10^{-8} centimeter.

A length of 10^{-8} centimeter (one hundred millionth of a centimeter), is called an *angstrom*. So the radius of the hydrogen atom is about one half of an angstrom.

Equation (89) shows that the radius of the orbit corresponding to any quantum number n is n^2 times the radius of the orbit for the ground state. Thus the ratios of the successive radii in order of size are 1:4:9:16: etc. The relative sizes of the possible orbits of the electron in the hydrogen atom are shown in the diagram on the next page.

Splitting of Lines

The Bohr model of the atom successfully explains why the spectrum of hydrogen has such discrete series of lines

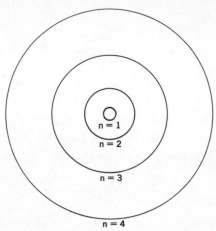

Possible circular orbits in the hydrogen atom, according to the Bohr theory

as the Lyman series, the Balmer series, etc. However, there are other known facts about the energy radiated by atoms that it leaves unexplained:

1. In the spectra of elements whose nuclear charge Z is greater than 1, where the Bohr theory predicts one spectral line there is actually a cluster of lines very close to each other.

2. When radiating atoms of an element are in a magnetic field, each line in the spectrum of the element is split into several lines. This splitting of the lines is known as the *normal Zeeman effect*.

3. In the spectra of heavy elements, a further splitting of each line into a pair of lines is observed. This additional splitting of lines is called the *fine structure* of the spectrum.

118

4. The lines in the spectrum of an element do not all have the same intensity.

To take into account items 1 and 2, Sommerfeld modified the Bohr theory by assuming that electron orbits in the atom may be ellipses as well as circles. To take into account item 3, Uhlenbeck and Goudsmidt assumed that an electron, besides revolving in its orbit, also spins like a top. To take into account item 4, an entirely new theory, known as *quantum mechanics,* was developed. The new theory retains Bohr's idea of energy levels in the atom. However, it discards the Bohr picture of electrons moving in orbits around the nucleus. Instead it pictures the nucleus as being surrounded by an *electron cloud* whose density varies from point to point. In this picture the density of the cloud at a point signifies the probability of finding an electron at that point. The development of the theory uses advanced mathematical techniques, but the results of the theory can be understood with the help of elementary mathematics only. Although the Bohr-Sommerfeld picture of the atom is not accurate, it is easier to visualize than the probability density picture. So it is now customary to use the physically inaccurate Bohr-Sommerfeld picture as a schematic diagram for the physically accurate quantum-mechanical results. We shall follow this custom when we summarize the main features of the quantum-mechanical model of the atom in the next chapter.

VII

The Electron Gets
a Permanent Wave

Dual Nature of Light

THE study of light has shown that it has a dual
character. It is a continuous *wave* moving through space,
but it is also a stream of discrete particles, the photons.
The wave character of light is revealed in such phenomena as the interference bands described on page 69.
The particle character of light is revealed in phenomena
like the photoelectric effect, described on page 99. The
connection between these two aspects of light is given by
equation (66) on page 101, which relates the momentum
M of the photon to the wavelength λ of the wave:
$M = h/\lambda$.

Electron Waves

In 1925 De Broglie used equation (66) as the point of
departure for a very bold hypothesis. He assumed that
just as light has both a particle and wave character, so
too does the electron. In fact, equation (66), solved for
λ, becomes $\lambda = h/M$, a formula for computing the wave-

length of an electron from its momentum. De Broglie's hypothesis was confirmed experimentally by Davisson and Germer, and others. Electrons do have a wavelength, and in fact, thin metal crystals behave like a diffraction grating for electron waves. They produce interference bands from which the wavelength can be calculated. The wavelength turns out to have precisely the value predicted by equation (66).

Standing Waves

The heart of the Bohr theory of the atom is the assumption that only those circular orbits are possible in which the angular momentum of the orbital motion of the electron has a value $nh/2\pi$, where n is a positive integer. This restriction, which is unexplained in the Bohr theory, can be explained in a natural way on the basis of the De Broglie hypothesis. Suppose an electron wave with wavelength λ is traveling around a circle whose radius r is large compared to λ. After each trip around, the wave retraces its steps around the circle. If, the second time around, a crest of the wave comes precisely where it did before, a stable wave configuration, known as a *standing wave,* is formed. This will occur only if the circumference of the circle is exactly a whole number times the wavelength. That is,

$$(92) \qquad\qquad 2\pi r = n\lambda,$$

where n is a positive integer. In circles where equation (92) is not satisfied, successive passages of the wave through any given point on the circle are out of step, and there is no stable configuration. The possible orbits of the

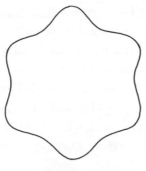

**Standing wave
(stable configuration)**

electron are those in which a standing wave can occur. In fact, Bohr's assumption, listed as 1B on page 112, can be derived from equation (92) as follows: By equation (66), $\lambda = h/M$. Substituting this value into equation (92), we get

$$(93) \qquad 2\pi r = \frac{nh}{M}.$$

Multiplying both sides of the equation by M, and dividing by 2π, we get

$$(94) \qquad Mr = \frac{nh}{2\pi}.$$

But, by equation (36) on page 68, $Mr = p =$ the angular momentum of the orbital motion of the electron, so equation (94) is the assumption 1B of Bohr's theory.

However, De Broglie's hypothesis was not used merely to patch up the Bohr theory. It was used as the starting point of an entirely new theory, known as *wave mechanics*, developed by Schrödinger and Dirac. Another theory, known as *matrix mechanics*, had also been developed by Heisenberg, Born, and Jordan, to take the place of the

Bohr theory. It has been shown that wave mechanics and matrix mechanics are mathematically equivalent. The name *quantum mechanics* is used to refer to the new theory of atomic structure in either of these two equivalent forms. We shall now summarize the principal features of the quantum-mechanical model of the atom, and we shall relate them to a schematic diagram in which the electron is pictured as moving in an elliptical orbit around the nucleus.

Quantum Numbers

As in the Bohr theory, there is a discrete series of energy levels at which an electron may stay in the atom. In the Bohr theory, each energy level is associated with a quantum number n. In the quantum-mechanical model, each energy level is associated with a set of four quantum numbers, designated by the symbols n, l, m, and σ (the Greek letter sigma). Each quantum number is related to a particular feature of the spectra of the elements, and a corresponding feature in the model of the atom. We now examine these quantum numbers, one at a time.

Size of the Orbit

The occurrence of discrete lines in the spectrum, as in the Balmer series of the hydrogen spectrum, shows that there are discrete energy levels in the atom. These levels depend in the first place on the *size* of the orbit of the electron. We use as a measure of the size of an elliptical orbit the length of its semi-major axis, shown in the dia-

124

gram below. The possible sizes are expressed in terms of the quantum number n, which may be any positive integer. So the possible values of n are 1, 2, 3, 4, etc. The larger the value of n is, the larger the size of the orbit is.

Shape of the Orbit

In atoms that are heavier than hydrogen, there is a cluster of lines where the Bohr theory predicts only one line. This splitting of the lines shows that there is a corresponding splitting of energy levels. The splitting of the energy levels arises from the fact that an ellipse of a given size may have many different shapes. The shape of an ellipse depends on the ratio of the length of the semi-

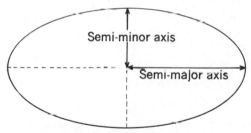

The major and minor axes of an ellipse

minor axis to the length of the semi-major axis. This ratio depends on the quantum number l. Just as only certain sizes of orbit are possible, only certain restricted shapes are possible. Only those shapes are possible which correspond to values of l that are whole numbers between 0 and $n - 1$ inclusive. There are n such values. So, for each quantum number n, there are n possible elliptical orbits that have the same size but different shapes. For

$n = 1$, there is only one possible orbit, with $l = 0$. For $n = 2$, there are two possible orbits, with $l = 0$, and $l = 1$, respectively. For $n = 3$, there are three possible orbits, with $l = 0$, $l = 1$, and $l = 2$, respectively; and so on. When $l = n - 1$, the orbit is a circle as in the Bohr theory. When l is less than $n - 1$, the orbit is a non-circular ellipse. The possible orbits, drawn to scale, are shown in the diagram below for $n = 1$, $n = 2$, and $n = 3$.

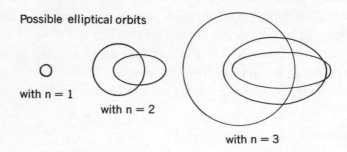

Possible elliptical orbits

with n = 1

with n = 2

with n = 3

The quantum number l is related to the angular momentum of the orbital motion of the electron. In fact, the magnitude of the angular moment is $\sqrt{l(l+1)}\ (h/2\pi)$. It is useful to represent the angular momentum by means

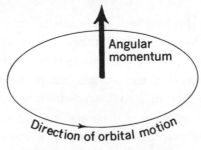

Angular momentum

Direction of orbital motion

Angular momentum as an arrow

126

of an arrow drawn along the axis around which the electron revolves. If we let each unit of length stand for $h/2\pi$, then the length of the arrow is made equal to $\sqrt{l(l+1)}$, to represent the magnitude of the angular momentum.

Tilted Orbits

The lines of the spectrum split when the atom is placed in a magnetic field H. The splitting of the lines shows that the magnetic field has caused a splitting of the energy level associated with each possible orbit. The

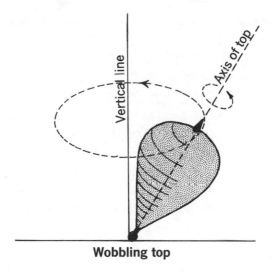

Wobbling top

electron revolving in its orbit constitutes an electric current. There is a magnetic field associated with this current. The magnetic field derived from the orbital motion of the electron interacts with the magnetic field H surrounding the atom. As a result of this interaction, the

127

orbit wobbles around the direction of H the way a spinning top tilted with respect to a vertical line wobbles around the line. The energy of the electron is altered by the energy of the wobbling motion of the orbit. The energy of the wobbling motion depends on how much the orbit is tilted. Only certain tilted positions of the orbit

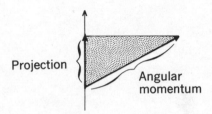

Projection

Angular momentum

Projection of angular momentum in direction of magnetic field

are possible. The position of the orbit is described in terms of the position of the angular momentum of the orbital motion of the electron. The angular momentum can have only those positions in which the length of its projection on the direction of H, expressed in units of $h/2\pi$, is an integer. The projection is represented by a positive integer when the projection and H have the same direction. It is represented by a negative integer when the projection and H are in opposite directions. The value of this integer is the quantum number m. Since the arrow representing the orbital angular momentum has length $\sqrt{l(l+1)}$ which is only slightly larger than l, the quantum number m may have only integral values between $-l$ and l inclusive. Thus when $l = 0$, m may have only one value, namely 0. When $l = 1$, m may have just three values, namely -1, 0, or 1. When $l = 2$, m may have only five values, namely -2, -1, 0, 1, and 2. In general, for any specified value of l, the number of possible values of m is $2l + 1$. The possible positions of the orbital angular momentum with respect to a given magnetic field H are shown in the diagram for the cases where $l = 1$, $l = 2$, and $l = 3$.

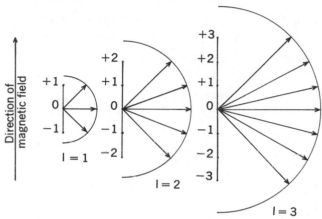

Possible positions of angular momentum arrow when I = 1, 2 and 3

Electron Spin

The further splitting of the spectral lines, known as the fine structure of the lines, shows that there is still more splitting of the energy levels in the atom. This splitting is accounted for by assuming that the electron spins like a top. Because of this spinning, the electron has a spin angular momentum whose magnitude, expressed in units of $h/2\pi$, turns out to be $\sqrt{\frac{1}{2}(\frac{1}{2} + 1)}$ (analogous to the magnitude $\sqrt{l(l + 1)}$ of the orbital

129

momentum). Because of the spinning, the electron is like a small magnet. As seen from the nucleus, the electron seems to be revolving in an orbit around the nucleus. As seen from the electron, the nucleus seems to be revolving around the electron. There is a magnetic field associated with this apparent orbital motion of the nucleus. The spinning electron interacts with this magnetic field. The energy of this interaction depends on how the spin angular momentum of the electron is tilted with respect to the orbital angular momentum. There are only two positions that the spin angular momentum can take, namely, those positions in which its projection on the direction of the orbital angular momentum has a length of $\frac{1}{2}$ or $-\frac{1}{2}$, expressed in units of $h/2\pi$. The length of this projection

is the fourth quantum number, and is denoted by the symbol σ. Thus, the quantum number σ has only two possible values, $\frac{1}{2}$ and $-\frac{1}{2}$, representing spin in opposite directions about the axis of spin.

The State of an Electron

To specify the condition or *state* of an electron in an atom it is necessary to specify the size and shape of its

130

orbit, the tilt of the orbit with respect to a given magnetic field, and the tilt of the spin angular momentum with respect to the orbital angular momentum. But these four properties of the electron are determined by the values of the quantum numbers n, l, m, and σ respectively. So a set of four numbers, each fixing the value of one of the quantum numbers, fixes the state of the electron. The table below summarizes the essential properties of an electron in an atom, the quantum number each is related to, and the values the quantum number may have.

Property of electron	Quantum number	Possible values
size of orbit	n	$1, 2, 3, \ldots$
shape of orbit	l	0 to $n - 1$
tilt of orbit	m	$-l$ to l
spin	σ	$\frac{1}{2}$ or $-\frac{1}{2}$

An important feature of the quantum-mechanical model of the atom is the rule that two electrons in an atom may not be in the same state. This rule is known as *Pauli's exclusion principle.* Another feature is the fact that when an atom is not excited, its electrons are in those states that correspond to the lowest possible energy levels. Using these rules, it is easy to picture how the electrons are arranged in any given atom. *In an atom of an element whose atomic number is Z there are Z electrons surrounding the nucleus. The Z electrons occupy the Z states that correspond to the lowest energy levels.*

Layers of Electrons

The quantum number n fixes the size of an electron's orbit. Consequently, electrons for which n has the same value are at about the same distance from the nucleus and form a layer or shell at that distance. In an atom that contains many electrons, the electrons are arranged in several shells. In each shell, the electrons for which the quantum number l has the same value form a sub-shell.

Each shell and sub-shell has room for only a limited number of electrons, which we can calculate by examining the possible values of the quantum numbers.

First shell ($n = 1$). Since the highest possible value of l is $n - 1$, which in this case is 0, there is only one possible value of l, namely 0. Since the possible values of m range from $-l$ to l, there is only one possible value of m, namely 0. There are two possible values of σ, namely $\frac{1}{2}$ and $-\frac{1}{2}$. So there is room in this shell for only two electrons.

Second shell ($n = 2$). The possible values of l are 0 and 1. In the sub-shell for which $l = 0$, m is also 0, and there are two choices of the value of σ. So there is room in this sub-shell for 2 electrons. In the sub-shell for which $l = 1$, m may have any one of the three values -1, 0, and 1, but for each choice of m there are two choices for σ. So there is room in this sub-shell for $2 \times 3 = 6$ electrons. Consequently the second shell has room for $2 + 6 = 8$ electrons.

Third shell ($n = 3$). The possible values of l are 0, 1, and 2. In the sub-shell for which $l = 0$, there is room for 2 elec-

132

			Spin:	
First shell {	n = 1	l = 0	m = 0	↻ or ↺
	n = 2	l = 0	m = 0	↻ or ↺
Second shell		l = 1	m = −1	↻ or ↺
			m = 0	↻ or ↺
			m = 1	↻ or ↺
	n = 3	l = 0	m = 0	↻ or ↺
		l = 1	m = −1	↻ or ↺
			m = 0	↻ or ↺
			m = 1	↻ or ↺
Third shell		l = 2	m = −2	↻ or ↺
			m = −1	↻ or ↺
			m = 0	↻ or ↺
			m = 1	↻ or ↺
			m = 2	↻ or ↺

Possible electron states in the first three shells of an atom

trons, as we have already seen. In the sub-shell for which $l = 1$, there is room for 6 electrons, as we have seen. In the sub-shell for which $l = 2$, m may have any one of the five possible values -2, -1, 0, 1, and 2, but for each choice of m there are two choices of σ. So there is room in this sub-shell for $2 \times 5 = 10$ electrons. Consequently the third shell has room for $2 + 6 + 10 = 18$ electrons.

133

Fourth shell ($n = 4$). The possible values of l are 0, 1, 2, and 3. The sub-shell for which $l = 0$ has room for 2 electrons. The sub-shell for which $l = 1$ has room for 6 electrons. The sub-shell for which $l = 2$ has room for 10 electrons. In the sub-shell for which $l = 3$, m may have

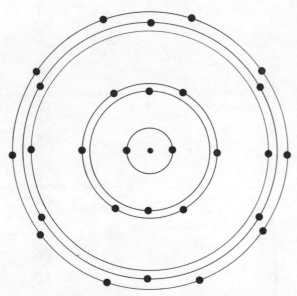

Schematic diagram of shell structure of an atom showing the first three shells and their subshells and the number of electrons that each has room for

any one of the seven possible values -3, -2, -1, 0, 1, 2, and 3, but for each choice of m there are two choices of σ. So there is room in this sub-shell for $2 \times 7 = 14$ electrons. Consequently the fourth shell has room for $2 + 6 + 10 + 14 = 32$ electrons.

Fifth shell ($n = 5$). The possible values of l are 0, 1, 2, 3, and 4. The sub-shells have room for 2, 6, 10, 14 and 18

134

electrons respectively. So the fifth shell has room for 50 electrons.

Sixth shell ($n = 6$). The possible value of l are 0, 1, 2, 3, 4 and 5. The sub-shells have room for 2, 6, 10, 14, 18, and 22 electrons respectively. So the sixth shell has room for 72 electrons.

Models of the Atoms

We are now ready to construct a model of the atom of each element. We examine the atoms one at a time, in order of increasing atomic number Z, the order in which they are listed in the periodic table. We follow the rule that the Z electrons in the atom occupy the Z states that correspond to the lowest energy levels. In general this means that they are in the lowest shells that have room for them. However, there are some exceptions, as we shall see.

$Z = 1$ (*hydrogen*). The atom contains 1 electron. The electron is in the first shell.

$Z = 2$ (*helium*). The atom contains 2 electrons. Both electrons are in the first shell. *The first shell is complete,* since it has room for only 2 electrons.

$Z = 3$ (*lithium*). The atom contains 3 electrons. Two electrons are in the first shell. The third electron is in the first sub-shell of the second shell.

$Z = 4$ (*beryllium*). The atom contains 4 electrons. Two electrons are in the first shell. The third and fourth electron are in the first sub-shell of the second shell.

135

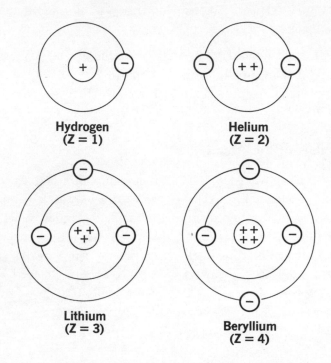

Hydrogen
(Z = 1)

Helium
(Z = 2)

Lithium
(Z = 3)

Beryllium
(Z = 4)

As Z is increased from 4 to 10, more and more electrons go into the second sub-shell of the second shell. When $Z = 10$ (neon), there are 2 electrons in the first shell and 8 electrons in the second shell. Then the second shell is complete, since it has room for only 8 electrons.

As Z is increased from 10 to 18, electrons begin to go into the third shell. When $Z = 18$ (argon), there are 2 electrons in the first shell, 8 electrons in the second shell, 2 electrons in the first sub-shell of the third shell, and 6 electrons in the second sub-shell of the third shell. Then the second sub-shell of the third shell is complete, since it has room for only 6 electrons.

136

When $Z = 19$ (potassium), the first 18 electrons are arranged as in argon. They fill the first two shells, and the first two sub-shells of the third shell. However, the 19th electron does not go into the third sub-shell of the third shell. It goes instead into the first sub-shell of the fourth shell. This is one of the exceptional cases where a lower energy level is found in a higher shell. There are other places, too, in the periodic table where places are left empty in a lower shell while electrons go into a higher shell. A particularly interesting set of examples occurs in the elements whose atomic numbers range from 57 to 71. In the atom whose atomic number is 57, there are 2 electrons in the first sub-shell of the sixth shell even though the fourth and fifth shells are not completely filled. As the atomic number is raised from 57 to 71, while there continue to be only 2 electrons in the sixth shell, more and more electrons go into the fourth shell until it is filled. So the atoms whose atomic numbers are between 57 and 71 inclusive all have two electrons in their outermost shell. They belong to the family of rare earths, and constitute the *lanthanide series* listed in the table on page 48.

Chemical Behavior

The arrangement of the electrons in the atoms in shells and sub-shells provides us with an explanation of why the elements behave chemically the way they do. The chemical behavior of an atom depends on the electrons in its outermost shell.

Completed sub-shells. In some atoms, the outermost

137

Number of Electrons in Each Shell and Sub-shell in the First 36 Atoms of the Periodic Table

Atomic Number	Element	n = 1	n = 2		n = 3			n = 4	
		l = 0	l = 0	l = 1	l = 0	l = 1	l = 2	l = 0	l = 1
1	H	1	—	—	—	—	—	—	—
2	He	2	—	—	—	—	—	—	—
3	Li	2	1	—	—	—	—	—	—
4	Be	2	2	—	—	—	—	—	—
5	B	2	2	1	—	—	—	—	—
6	C	2	2	2	—	—	—	—	—
7	N	2	2	3	—	—	—	—	—
8	O	2	2	4	—	—	—	—	—
9	F	2	2	5	—	—	—	—	—
10	Ne	2	2	6	—	—	—	—	—
11	Na	2	2	6	1	—	—	—	—
12	Mg	2	2	6	2	—	—	—	—
13	Al	2	2	6	2	1	—	—	—
14	Si	2	2	6	2	2	—	—	—
15	P	2	2	6	2	3	—	—	—
16	S	2	2	6	2	4	—	—	—
17	Cl	2	2	6	2	5	—	—	—
18	A	2	2	6	2	6	—	—	—
19	K	2	2	6	2	6	—	1	—
20	Ca	2	2	6	2	6	—	2	—
21	Sc	2	2	6	2	6	1	2	—
22	Ti	2	2	6	2	6	2	2	—
23	V	2	2	6	2	6	3	2	—
24	Cr	2	2	6	2	6	5	1	—
25	Mn	2	2	6	2	6	5	2	—
26	Fe	2	2	6	2	6	6	2	—
27	Co	2	2	6	2	6	7	2	—
28	Ni	2	2	6	2	6	8	2	—
29	Cu	2	2	6	2	6	10	1	—
30	Zn	2	2	6	2	6	10	2	—
31	Ga	2	2	6	2	6	10	2	1
32	Ge	2	2	6	2	6	10	2	2
33	As	2	2	6	2	6	10	2	3
34	Se	2	2	6	2	6	10	2	4
35	Br	2	2	6	2	6	10	2	5
36	Kr	2	2	6	2	6	10	2	6

shell contains just enough electrons to fill the first two sub-shells of this shell, namely 8 electrons. This happens in helium, neon, argon, krypton, xenon, and radon, in which the electrons are grouped in completed sub-shells as shown in the list below:

Helium:	2.	$Z = 2$
Neon:	2; 2, 6.	$Z = 10$
Argon:	2; 2, 6; 2, 6.	$Z = 18$
Krypton:	2; 2, 6; 2, 6, 10; 2, 6.	$Z = 36$
Xenon:	2; 2, 6; 2, 6, 10; 2, 6, 10; 2, 6.	$Z = 54$
Radon:	2; 2, 6; 2, 6, 10; 2, 6, 10, 14; 2, 6, 10; 2, 6.	$Z = 86$

This outer ring of 8 electrons is a very stable configuration and tends not to interact with the electrons in other atoms. As a result, these elements are chemically inert, that is, they enter into almost no chemical combinations. They are the noble gases found in the last column of the periodic table.

Valence. Some atoms have an electron configuration that is almost like that of a noble gas, except that there are a few more electrons outside the configuration. These atoms tend to lose the outer electrons easily, and are chemically active. The number of electrons outside the noble gas configuration is the valence of the atom. For example, lithium has the helium configuration plus one more electron; sodium has the neon configuration plus one more electron; potassium has the argon configuration plus one more electron. So lithium, sodium, and potassium tend to lose one electron. Each has valence one, and they belong to the family of alkali metals.

Some atoms have an electron configuration that is almost like that of a noble gas, except that there are some unfilled places in the outermost sub-shell. These atoms tend to gain electrons to fill the empty places, and so are chemically active. The number of empty places in the outermost sub-shell is the valence of the atom. For example, fluorine has one fewer electron than the neon configuration; chlorine has one fewer electron than the argon configuration; bromine has one fewer electron than the krypton configuration. So fluorine, chlorine, and bromine tend to gain one electron. Each has valence one, and they belong to the family of halogens.

Ions. An atom that has gained or lost electrons becomes an ion. For example, a lithium atom that has lost one electron becomes the ion Li^+. Since the configuration of electrons in Li^+ is like that in helium, the theory predicts that the spectra of helium and Li^+ should resemble each other, which, indeed, they do. A fluorine atom that has gained one electron becomes the ion Fl^-. Since the configuration of electrons in Fl^- is like that in neon, the theory predicts that the spectra of neon and Fl^- should resemble each other, and, in fact, they do.

If we list the chemical elements in order of atomic number, we encounter atoms with completed outer sub-shells over and over again: first helium, then neon, etc. Each of these is preceded by an atom which is one electron short of having the same configuration. It is also followed by an atom which has one electron over and above that configuration. That is why the halogens, the noble gases, and the alkali metals occur *periodically* in the list of elements arranged by atomic number. The rare earth elements all have two electrons in the outermost shell. That is why they are so much alike chemically. There are fifteen of them, but there is only one place in the table where they belong. That is why they are listed

140

separately below the periodic table on page 48. Thus the theory of the shell structure of the atom serves to explain both the order and the imperfections of the periodic table of the elements.

INDEX

Index

145